THE HISTORY OF MEDICINE SERIES
ISSUED UNDER THE AUSPICES
OF THE LIBRARY OF THE
NEW YORK ACADEMY OF MEDICINE

No. 21

Observations on Some of
THE MOST FREQUENT
AND IMPORTANT
DISEASES OF THE
HEART

By
ALLAN BURNS

With an introduction by
DICKINSON W. RICHARDS, M.D.

Published under the auspices of the Library of
The New York Academy of Medicine

HAFNER PUBLISHING COMPANY
New York   London
1964

Originally published 1809, *Edinburgh*

Reprinted 1964 *with new introduction*

Printed and Published by
Hafner Publishing Company, Inc.
31 East 10th Street
New York, N.Y. 10003

Library of Congress Catalogue Card #63-16677

Introduction © Copyright 1964 by the New York Academy
of Medicine, Library

Lithographed in the U.S.A.
by NOBLE OFFSET PRINTERS, INC.
New York, N. Y. 10003

INTRODUCTION TO 1964 REPRINT

In his brief life span of thirty-one years, Allan Burns made scientific contributions of major importance in anatomy, pathology, surgery, and medicine; and this in the face of obstacles and frustrations that would have turned back any but the most dauntless.

He was born September 18, 1781, in Glasgow, the son of the Rev. John Burns. At 14, he began the study of medicine. Two years later he abandoned his formal studies to become the laboratory assistant, the "director of the dissecting rooms," for his older brother Dr. John Burns, who was soon to be the leading surgeon in the city.

The younger brother was a keen and skillful dissector, avid in his desire for knowledge, keeping careful case records, notes, and drawings. One is reminded of that other student, three hundred years before, who also in his earliest years displayed the same intense, almost fanatical desire to discover the secrets of human anatomy by actual dissection,—Andreas Vesalius.

In 1804, young Burns, then 23 years old, received an extraordinary message. The Empress Catherine of Russia, wife of Czar Alexander I, invited him to come to St. Petersburg, as director and surgeon of a new hospital, to be run along the English plan. Burns accepted, went to Russia, stayed there six months trying to carry out this new assignment, then resigned and returned to Glasgow.

He arrived to find that his distinguished brother John Burns, having been charged with the felonious offense of body snatching, had been disbarred from giving further lectures in anatomy; although, through the somewhat mysterious logic of British law, he continued to practice surgery undisturbed, and a few years after was appointed professor of surgery at the University.

At all events, Allan took on the lectures in anatomy, apparently with considerable success. There was, in fact, during these years in Glasgow a resurgence of interest in the medical sciences. It is recorded that in 1814 there were eight hundred students in anatomy alone. Even London, still in the great era of John Hunter, William Heberden, and Edward Jenner, looked with a mixture of surprise and envy on its up-country cousin. It was a lively and exuberant medical community, in which scientific zeal at times exceeded strictly legal bounds. In his delightful essay on Allan Burns,[1] James B. Herrick has this to say about anatomy in Glasgow in those days: "Whereas in London a student might wait for a month for a cadaver, in Glasgow he seldom waited. Some bodies supplied in the latter city were corpses of criminals or panders. In addition there was a brisk trade with Ireland [!]. That bodies were often obtained by exhumation was suspected, if not admitted or proved."

[1] J. B. Herrick, Allan Burns, 1781-1813, Anatomist, Surgeon, and Cardiologist, *Bull. Soc. Med. Hist.*, 4: 457-483, 1935.

Burns also resumed the writing of anatomical and clinical papers, which he had begun as early as 1802. He was a close student of Morgagni and Lieutaud, and was acquainted with the work of the pathologists of his day; and in medicine he was a devoted follower of the great English clinicians of the generation just then coming to a close, especially John Hunter and Caleb Parry. His industry as a pathologist must have been prodigious, to judge from the wide experience which he called upon and quoted in his writings. He also sought and used everything that he could learn, from his friends as well as from written records. At first thought, one is surprised that Burns apparently knew nothing of the essay on the heart [2] published in 1806 by the great French clinician Jean-Nicolas Corvisart. Whereas this latter work was conspicuously deficient in any description of coronary artery disease, on other conditions,—cardiac enlargement, congestive failure, aneurysm, etc.,—it covered much the same ground that Burns's essay did. During these years, however, Britain and France were at war, and communication was probably difficult. A review of Corvisart's essay finally appeared in the *Edinburgh Medical and Surgical Journal* in January, 1811.

Allan Burns held no degree and was never qualified to practice medicine or surgery. In spite of this, he managed somehow to do a great deal of actual surgery, both minor and major, as his writings openly declare. He "attended" his brother's patients, as Her-

[2] Jean-Nicolas Corvisart, *Essai sur les maladies et les lésions organiques du coeur* . . . Paris, 1806. Engl. tr. New York: Hafner, 1962.

rick expresses it, and "drew on" his medical and surgical friends to provide further opportunities.

He wrote two books, and these contain most of his important contributions: the present volume on diseases of the heart, which was published in 1809; and his *Observations on the Surgical Anatomy of the Head and Neck,* which appeared two years later.

As early as 1810, his health, which was never robust, began to fail. He was troubled with "dyspeptic symptoms"; and developed pains in his right iliac region, "perfectly fixed, and so local that he could cover it with the point of a finger." (Was there ever a better description of McBurney's point?). He struggled on for three years, and somehow kept at work. Finally, an abscess burst into his rectum, he became febrile, with diarrhea, and died. Autopsy showed localized peritonitis, presumably from a ruptured appendix, with abscess formation.

Herrick thus summarizes (p. 482) the major achievements of Allan Burns: "The coronary artery theory of angina pectoris, and his experiment with ligatures, his clear statement of the back pressure theory of dilatation and hypertrophy, whether from valvular obstruction or leakage, and his discussion of ante-mortem thrombi, aortic aneurysm, the falciform ligament, postmortem digestion, and the ligation of the thyroid arteries for goitre, are all notable contributions."

The small volume that is here republished has a very lengthy title, as the first page shows, but the book itself is simply and clearly written, and needs but little in the way of introduction. It is presented by the author in the form of lectures to his students, and to them he very kindly and courteously dedicates the work. The style is discursive, sometimes a little verbose, sometimes repetitive, but not more than would be expected of a lecturer emphasizing a certain point.

The first chapter is chiefly concerned with congenital malformations, and is introduced with a remarkably lucid description of "imperfect arterialization of the blood" (he apologizes for this "uncouth term"), and the distinction between those forms caused by pulmonary disorders, and those caused by congenital malformations with true venous admixture. He proceeds then to discuss the major congenital malformations: transposition of the aorta, patent ductus arteriosus, patent foramen ovale, and cor biloculare. He includes also organic mitral stenosis, and of course is not able here to distinguish congenital from acquired disease.

The next three sections, on dilatation of the heart, including those associated with pericardial adhesions and pericardial effusion, are remarkable for the clear conception of congestive failure. It may be noted that Corvisart, who was lecturing in Paris at about the same time, had reached a similar appreciation of the congestive state.

After two rather diffuse sections on diminution in heart size and on its changes in structure, Burns writes his greatest medical contribution, the "Observations on disease of the Coronary Arteries and on Syncope Anginosa." He himself claims nothing new beyond what had been written by Parry and Heberden, but actually his physiological conception is clearer, as evidenced by his famous comparison of a coronary seizure with the state of a skeletal muscle following an arterial ligature. This is a remarkable chapter, and with the use of many actual case histories Burns gives a clinical picture which is more detailed, and just as vivid, as Heberden's classical description, which had been first published forty years before.

The later chapters of the book, on valvular heart disease, and on aneurysm of the thoracic aorta, not only reveal the author's precise clinical and pathological observations, but display how broad an experience he had been able to accumulate. Through all the work, there are of course faulty assumptions and conclusions of various kinds, as well as antiquated therapy which was a part of the medicine of that day.

The section on preternatural pulsations in the epigastrium is a nice clinical exercise in differential diagnosis, and the last, on anomalous distribution of certain peripheral arteries, is a series of demonstrations in anatomy, for the use and instruction of his surgical colleagues.

DICKINSON W. RICHARDS

OBSERVATIONS

ON

SOME OF THE MOST FREQUENT AND IMPORTANT DISEASES OF THE

HEART;

ON

ANEURISM OF THE THORACIC AORTA;

ON

PRETERNATURAL PULSATION IN THE EPIGASTRIC REGION:

AND ON

THE UNUSUAL ORIGIN AND DISTRIBUTION OF SOME OF THE LARGE ARTERIES OF THE HUMAN BODY.

Illustrated by Cases.

BY ALLAN BURNS,

MEMBER OF THE ROYAL COLLEGE OF SURGEONS, LONDON; AND LECTURER
ON ANATOMY AND SURGERY, GLASGOW.

EDINBURGH:

PRINTED BY JAMES MUIRHEAD,

FOR THOMAS BRYCE AND CO. MEDICAL BOOKSELLERS, No. 3,
INFIRMARY STREET; JOHN MURRAY, FLEET STREET, AND
J. CALLOW, CROWN COURT, PRINCE'S STREET, SOHO,
LONDON.

1809

TO THE

GENTLEMEN WHO HAVE ATTENDED, AND
WHO ARE AT PRESENT ATTENDING THE
AUTHOR'S LECTURES ON ANATOMY
AND SURGERY.

GENTLEMEN,

THERE are none to whom
I could with equal propriety inscribe the
following OBSERVATIONS on the DISEASES
of the HEART, as to you to whom they were
originally addressed, and for whose use they
are now chiefly made public. In Lecturing
on this subject, I noticed, that although
many detached Works have been published
on particular affections of the Heart, still
no treatise has yet appeared, presenting a
connected view of the causes and consequences, of the various Diseases to which
this most important organ is liable. These
considerations, in the first instance, led me
to pay some attention to this subject; and
the same considerations, have now induced
me to make the result of my inquiries public.

ON reviewing these OBSERVATIONS, I see
much occasion to apologize for the imperfec-

tion of the information they contain; however, such as they are, if they shall, in any degree, tend to facilitate the study of this branch of Morbid Anatomy, or lead to a rational mode of treatment, I shall have fully attained the purpose I had in view, in laying them before the Public.

I am,

GENTLEMEN,

with much regard,

Your sincere friend,

ALLAN BURNS.

GLASGOW, 24th January, }
1809.

CONTENTS.

Page.

General Observations on Diseases of the Heart,   1

Observations on Uniform Enlargement, and on Dilatation of the Heart 39

Observations on Partial Dilatation of the Heart   50

Observations on Chronic Inflammation of the Heart   58

Observations on the Effects produced by the Diminution of the Size of the Heart 109

Observations on the consequences resulting from change in the Structure of the Substance of the Heart 117

Observations on Disease of the Coronary Arteries, and on Syncope Anginosa 136

Observations on the Effects resulting from change of Structure of the Valves of the Heart, and Large Arteries 163

Observations on the Formation of Polypi in the Heart 191

Observations on Aneurism of the Thoracic Aorta   203

Remarks on the Causes of Preternatural Pulsation in the Epigastrium 262

Remarks on the Unusual Origin and Course of some of the Large and Important Arteries of the Human Body 278

ERRATA.

Page 3. Line 3, for "order," *read* "organ."
—— 62. —— 22, dele "is."
—— 84. —— 24, for "digging," *read* "dragging."
—— 116. —— 12, for "serous," *read* "aqueous."
—— 116. —— 13, for "aqueous," *read* "serous."
—— 117. —— 19, for "recorded," *read* "reversed."
—— 133. —— 11, for "auricle or," *read* "auricular."
—— 177. —— 26, for "left," *read* "felt."
—— 179. —— 20, for "micæ," *read* "vomicæ."

OBSERVATIONS

ON

DISEASES OF THE HEART.

======

THE heart, from the intricacy of its structure, and from its incessant action, is liable to
many diseases, and these from the importance
of the function of this organ, are at all times
highly alarming. Some of them are extremely
insidious in their commencement, are attended
with obscure and perplexing symptoms, and in
their result are almost uniformly and speedily
fatal. These have often the appearance of
being produced by a morbid state of some
other organ than of the heart, but in their result they are almost uniformly and speedily

A

fatal. Others again are abrupt and decided in their attack, but continue for a great length of time, before they produce fatal effects. It becomes, therefore, a matter of much importance with the medical practitioner, to be able to distinguish diseases of the heart from affections of other parts; and to know the facts which are to regulate his prognosis. For the purpose of arrangement, diseases of the heart may be divided into three classes;

THE first class containing the sympathetic affections of the heart, or those diseases which are dependent on the consent which this organ has with other parts of the body;

THE second, those affections which are brought on by such malconformations of the heart, as give rise to a mixture of the venous with the arterial blood; and,

THE third, those diseases induced by some organic affection of the heart which mechanically impairs the circulation, but does not necessarily alter the composition or properties of the blood.

IT is not my intention to lay before you any remarks at this time on the First of these classes; and in treating of the other two, I shall endeavour to select only the most frequent and important diseases for particular discussion, and chiefly such as I have myself had an opportunity of seeing.

THE symptoms characterizing the Second class of diseases of the heart, may be produced not only by malconformation of this order, but also to a certain degree, by whatever offers a mechanical obstruction to the performance of the respiratory function. Thus, extensive and close adhesion of the pleura pulmonalis to the pleura costalis, will, as we learn from an interesting case by Dr. Marcet, induce symptoms which mark a deficiency of the arterial principle in the blood.* Whatever, also, has a tendency to encroach on the bronchial cells, will, according to the extent of the compression, produce symptoms which indicate, if I may be permitted to use the uncouth term, imperfect arterialization of the blood. Hence the bloated livid countenance in pulmonic anasarca, and the inflated purple face so universally attendant on pneumonia or inflammation of the lungs. In these diseases, obscure symptoms are produced of an affection of the heart, without any real disease of this organ. The same takes place when the lungs are compressed by effusion of water or secretion of pus into the chest, by solid tumors formed in the thorax, by enlargement of the abdominal viscera, or by

---

* In employing the term *arterial principle,* I do not wish to be understood as representing, that the arterial blood differs from the venous, merely in possessing some peculiar principle. The term is used in a general sense, to denote the aggregate of qualities, which distinguish arterial from venous blood.

accumulation of water in the belly. These are only temporary, and indirect causes, producing a morbid state of the circulating fluids; but the same diseased condition of the blood, is permanently kept up by several malconformations of the heart.

FROM the enumeration of the causes producing a deficiency of the arterial principle in the blood, it will, at first sight, appear to you, that they are divisible into two classes. In the first class, this state of the blood is occasioned by the existence of some mechanical obstacle to the action of the lungs, by which the due arterialization of the blood is prevented. But, in the second, which more immediately interests us, the same state of the circulating fluids is induced by a direct mixture of the venous with the arterial blood. You will therefore readily understand, that in the one case, the blood is duly sent into the lungs, to be rendered arterial, but owing to the deficiency of oxygen, this process is imperfectly performed; in the other, owing to some malconformation of the heart, or large vessels, a part of the blood passes directly from the venous into the arterial circulation. Although, therefore, the proper quantity of air may in the latter case enter the bronchiæ, still its presence in them is rendered of no avail by the peculiar formation of the vascular system.

THE symptoms denoting a mixture of the venous with the arterial blood, do not, except where the preponderance of the former is very great, make their appearance for some weeks, or often months, after birth; but, as soon as they occur, they indicate clearly the nature of the affection. The breathing is performed with difficulty, the parts covered by the delicate epidermis lose their natural colour, and assume a livid tint, while the limbs and trunk become of a leaden hue. The child at the same time is averse to motion, which aggravates the symptoms, is affected with a short suffocating or stifling cough, like that in peripneumony or hooping cough. The expectoration is but slight, although occasionally blood is brought up by the violence of the exertion. The animal functions are all of them languid, the bowels are torpid, the nervous system is depressed, and the heat of the body is reduced below what it naturally is; such are the permanent effects produced by imperfectly arterialized blood. The symptoms do not however remain constantly in this state, but are subject, after irregular intervals, to exacerbations, during which, the heart palpitates, the chest feels constricted, the breathing is oppressed, the head is pained, the eyes are prominent, the lips, ears, nose, tongue, and the parts beneath the nails become very dark in their colour; nay, in cases of extreme urgency, they acquire a purplish black hue. The anxiety is insufferable, the urine and fæces come away involuntarily, the body feels cold to a by-stander, and appears as if it were on the eve of parting with life. The arterial system acts feebly, the jugular veins are turgid, the countenance is inflated, and resembles that of a person suffering strangulation; the convulsive motions of the limbs indicate the greatest agitation, both of body and mind. This state cannot long remain in full force; therefore, after a shorter or longer continuance, the system falls into a state of quiescence, from which it gradually emerges, continues languid and torpid, and the surface is permanently of a darker colour than it ought to be. On the application of any trivial, and frequently without any obvious cause, the train of symptoms already mentioned recur. In proportion as the child advances in years, the paroxysms become more frequent, more violent, and the remissions less perfect, till at last, upon the supervention of dropsical symptoms, the constitution is completely worn out.

HAVING thus, in a general way, described the effects of a deficiency of the arterial principle in the blood, let us select one species of mal-constructed heart; that wherein the fœtal conformation remains during adult age, and let us endeavour to explain the causes of those symptoms with which it is accompanied. Upon the contraction of the right ventricle, the venous blood is pushed on towards the lungs, but here we must trace the consequences of the ductus arteriosus remaining open. In this case, the blood finds much less resistance to its passage into the aorta, than it does to circulate along the ramifications of the pulmonary vessels; hence one cause why venous blood is intermixed with arterial, but not the only one, for an equal portion passes through the foramen ovale into the left auricle, and this for the express purpose of continuing the equilibrium of distension. Now, from this short statement, it must be obvious, that sooner or later, an accumulation of blood highly venous must take place in the arterial system; and whenever this proceeds a certain length, we are prepared to understand why the body feels weak; why the pulse flutters, and the heart vibrates; why the vital functions are nearly arrested; and why the person expresses the greatest anxiety and oppression in the chest, referable in part to the presence of venous blood in the left side of the heart, but equally occasioned by the consent which obtains between this organ and the lungs. Such is the general explanation of the cause of the occurrence of a paroxysm. Let me next observe, that whatever renders the circulation irregular, accelerates the accession of a fit, as then, from the increased frequency of the vascular contractions, blood comes to be more rapidly transmitted through the heart, and thus venous blood is poured more frequently into the arterial system, inducing thus, in a shorter time, the train of symptoms which would inevitably have followed, though at a somewhat more remote period.

FROM this slight sketch, you will readily conceive that whatever agitates either body or mind, must be pernicious, as thereby a recurrence of the symptoms already mentioned, will be induced; and further we conclude, that in such a case, medical aid can avail but little. Strict attention to diet, to avoid whatever is indigestible, an absolute prohibition of all spirituous cordials or wines, unless prescribed in a medical point of view, together with a watchful care as to restraining irregular sallies of passion, comprise all that can be said of palliative means. I say palliative, for here, while the morbid formation of the heart remains, a radical cure is physically impossible. Oxy-muriate of potass, and such other substances, as in a small volume contain a large proportion of oxygen, and are readily made to part with it, have indeed been recommended on an imperfect hypothesis, but have failed, as might, without any superior discriminating powers, have been predicted.

It is worthy of observation, that in the diseases belonging to this class, when the patient is apparently just expiring, he is in reality bettering his condition. Mr. John Bell explains with accuracy and spirit, the changes which take place during the paroxysm. The common respiration, as he observes, will not suffice; the venous blood is gaining on the arterial system; therefore, the lungs must be as completely emptied as possible, the air is accordingly forcibly expelled, the child sinks exhausted, soon he breathes again, but expires with equal exertion as formerly. This struggle continues for a length of time; at last, respiration seems suspended; during this suspension, the surface gradually loses its livid colour, and becomes more of the pale leaden hue. Then the patient fetches a deep sigh, recovery begins, and goes on apace, till at length he is as well as circumstances will permit. While these phenomena are going on, we learn from Mr. Bell, that the child is expelling portion after portion of the contaminated air from the lungs, till finally he succeeds in introducing such a quantity of pure air, as will in some measure restore the balance of arterial and venous blood. Nor is it only by calling into forcible action the natural auxiliary muscles of expiration, that the patient endeavours to make way for the introduction of an extra quantity of atmospheric air into the lungs; he also lessens the capacity of the chest, if he be very young, by turning on his belly, or if he be older he presses his breast firmly against a table, or any solid object. By these means, which an ignorant spectator considers as of no value, the contaminated air is driven out, new

air admitted, relief obtained, and on every occurrence of the paroxysm, the patient has recourse to similar means.

FROM this view of the matter, it might perhaps be advisable to desire the patient to inhale
either pure oxygen gas, or a mixture of this
and atmospheric air. This, if oxygen were all
that was wanted, might restore the balance of
arterial and venous blood, sooner than if the
process were left to nature. I would not, however, have you be too sanguine in your expectation of alleviating the sufferings of the patient, by this treatment. It is probable that in
a person having the heart malformed, there is a
want of capability on the part of the lungs, to
alter the constitution of the blood more rapidly
than they would do, were the patient left to
struggle with the paroxysm. The lungs do
not serve the purposes of mere chemical ma-
trasses, digesting blood and gases together; no,
they assuredly perform a more elevated function; they, by their vital action, destroy the existing affinities, separate the component parts
of the atmospheric air into their integral parti-
cles, and apply these to the purposes they are
destined to serve in the animal economy. Although therefore we distend the bronchiæ with
oxygen gas, still if we cannot increase the action of the pulmonary vessels, the blood will
not be more speedily deprived of its noxious
qualities than it would have been, had we not

interfered. It is therefore more necessary to warn you against officiously endeavouring to assist nature, than to persuade you of the propriety of a prompt interference being required on the part of the practitioner. If any medical treatment be really necessary, it can only be to supply the lungs with purer air, but how far this will be advantageous to the patient, must be determined by future observation.

HAVING made these preliminary remarks on the causes and consequences of imperfect arterialization of the blood, I am prepared to enter into a detail of the different species of malconformation of the heart, which give rise to this morbid condition of the circulating fluids.

THE following are the species of these malconformations, which it is my intention to treat of in succession:

Species First.—Where the aorta originates equally from the right and left ventricle.

Species Second.—Where the foramen ovale and ductus arteriosus remain open.

Species Third.—Where the ductus arteriosus is obliterated, but the foramen ovale remains pervious; or a preternatural opening leads from the one ventricle to the other.

Species Fourth.—Where the pulmonary artery is impervious at its origin, but still receives a small portion of blood by a retrograde action of the ductus arteriosus.

Species Fifth.—Where the heart merely consists of two cavities, an auricle and ventricle, and where from the latter, a vessel originates which afterwards divides into two branches, one to the lungs the other to the body.

Species Sixth.—Where the mitral valve is malformed, leaving merely a small opening, leading from the left auricle into the ventricle.

UNDER one or other of these species, all the varieties of malconformation which have been met with, and which give rise to imperfect arterialization of the blood may be arranged.—Were I to enter, however, into a full description of each species, and to collect the different examples of them on record, it would occupy a much larger portion of time than we can now bestow on the enquiry;—I therefore only propose to offer a few observations on the different species, and to illustrate each by the narration of one or two cases.

IN the first species, where the aorta originates equally from the right and left ventricles, the mode in which the malconfo mation deranges the constitution of the blood, is so evident, that it would be a waste of time to enlarge upon the subject. It is obvious, if the aorta rises by one limb from the right, and by another from the left ventricle, that as the contraction of these cavities is synchronous, a mixture of venous and arterial blood, must at each contraction be propelled into the great artery, and this mixed fluid when circulated through the body, will produce all that terrible train of symptoms which have already been described, as attendant on a deficiency of the vital principle in the blood. The aorta has been found originating from both ventricles, by Sandifort, as well as by Dr. Nevin of Down Patrick. The preparation of this species of malconformation which occurred to Dr. Nevin, is in the possession of Dr. Jeffray, the justly esteemed professor of anatomy in this University. In both of these instances, the person led a most miserable life, and was subject on every trivial exertion to those paroxysms which are produced by a mixture of the venous with the arterial blood, and at length died with dropsical symptoms.

Species Second.—WHERE the foramen ovale and ductus arteriosus remain each of them pervious after birth, or during adult age.

THESE apertures are useful only in the œconomy of the fœtus, and consequently we generally observe, that soon after delivery a process commences to remove them. This in the case of the foramen ovale, consists in the adhesion of the valve to the septum of the auricle, while the ductus arteriosus is obliterated by being changed into an impervious ligament, which connects the pulmonary artery to the aorta. This salutary process does not however invariably take place; occasionally we meet with examples wherein the ductus arteriosus, and oval aperture remain open after birth, and whenever this happens, the imperfection in the structure of the heart is marked by symptoms more or less urgent, according to the extent of their exciting cause. Let us, however, inquire what purposes these serve in the œconomy of the fœtal circulation. A very superficial view, will convince any one that they are placed there for the express purpose of maintaining the equilibrium of magnitude in the two sides of the heart, and this they accomplish in the following manner:

IN the unborn child, the lungs have no play; they lie in the chest torpid, compressed, and totally inactive; they are, previous to birth, altogether useless to the fœtus, and their place is supplied by another organ, which is in part formed by the mother, in part by the child, and which is named Placenta. Now, from this collapsed state of the lungs, we find that they are incapable of transmitting with ease, or even with safety the whole mass of blood through them. But how is this obviated? very simply, by directing the current of blood into a new channel, by sending a portion of it directly from the pulmonary artery into the aorta, by means of the ductus arteriosus, which is a tube, as you have already seen, extended from the one to the other. We have thus removed the superfluous quantity of blood from the fœtal lungs, but I must next mention that this is a temporary provision, and beneficial only to the fœtus. As soon as the child is born, its lungs, hitherto inactive, are excited to vigorous action; the bronchiæ are fully distended with air; the ductus arteriosus has its use superseded; the whole of the blood sent out by the right auricle can now circulate through the lungs, and pass by the circuitous rout of the pulmonary circulation into the aorta. But as the left auricle, while the fœtus remained in utero, received only two thirds of the blood sent out by the pulmonary artery, it follows, that without some provision, this cavity shall be capable of containing no more after birth. To guard against this occurrence, however, the foramen ovale is added; the ductus arteriosus and oval aperture balance each other; an equal portion of blood is sent by the foramen ovale into the left auricle, as is transmitted by the ductus arteriosus into the aorta; and by this contrivance, without overloading the lungs, without deranging the œconomy of the fœtal vascular system, the two auricles are maintained of equal size ; the left is made capable of receiving after birth all the blood sent out by the right. The moment.

however, that the lungs are called into exertion, the instant that the placenta ceases to act, the ductus arteriosus, and foramen ovale, become hurtful, and in general a series of operations are begun by which they may be obliterated.

IN some rare cases, the foramen ovale and ductus arteriosus remain pervious; the right side still continues to mix its contents with the pure blood of the left, producing the symptoms which characterize imperfect arterialization of the blood. To understand how this happens, we have only to revert to the fœtal conformation of the heart. In the unborn child, the right auricle receives the blood from the umbilical vein, or that vessel which returns this fluid from the placenta; of consequence, the right side contains, previous to birth, the purest blood; but not so after the child is born ; then the lungs perform their own specific function; in them the venous blood is arterialized, and returns after this change to the left side of the heart. After birth, the continuance of the fœtal circulation is in the highest degree prejudicial, as we may learn from the history of the following case, which came under my own view, and the preparation of which is now in the possession of my friend Dr. Monro, jun.

JAMES MELLIS, was to appearance, when born, a healthy and robust child, but scarce had he attained his third year, ere he began to manifest signs of disease, which increased as he advanced in years, and finally carried him to his grave. The first morbid symptoms were chiefly perceived in the muscular system. If at any time he over-exerted himself in his youthful amusements, he was instantly seized with spasmodic twitches in his muscles, accompanied with urgent cough and reiterated fits of dyspnœa, and occasionally during the violence of paroxysm, the colour of the skin would be observed to change to a faint purple or a slightly livid hue; cessation from exertions in general, proved sufficient to restore the functions to their natural state, but a repetition of the exciting cause was in general followed by a recurrence of the morbid phenomena. During the three first years of his life, he passed through the usual infantile diseases, and suffered severely from the small pox. The occurrence of these, however, did not produce any material alteration in the complexion of the permanent complaint, of which the symptoms remained with little alteration for the space of forty or forty-two years.

DURING the whole of this period, he had been able to follow his usual employment, which was that of a painter, but latterly had acquired a torpid and unhealthy appearance. The symptoms increased in urgency; the paroxysms recurred more frequently than formerly; and were excited by the operation of the most trivial causes.

The countenance was permanently purplish and bloated, and constantly during the continuance of the paroxysms, the lips, the skin beneath the nails, and all those parts covered by delicate epidermis, were of the darkest purple, and the oppression and anxiety in the chest became intolerable; the vital functions were imperfectly discharged, general œdema supervened; the body was almost incessantly bedewed with a cold and clammy sweat; the appetite failed; the pulse became small, feeble, and hardly perceptible; the debility was extreme; the anxiety and oppression rapidly increased, and during the winter of 1799, he died.

WE were naturally desirous to ascertain the the nature of the affection, and permission was obtained to inspect the body. On examination, the thorax was found to contain about a pound of an aqueous fluid of a yellowish tinge. The lungs were every where sound and free from adhesions. The pericardium contained about two ounces of a darker coloured fluid than what was effused into the chest, but the principal morbid appearances were discovered in the heart and large vessels. The *ductus arteriosus* and foramen ovale were found to be open. The former equalled in size a large crow quill, the latter the circumference of the barrel of a goose quill, a circumstance easily accounted for, if we recollect the difference of velocity, and impetus of the circulation in the auricles and arteries.

THE brain and abdominal viscera were perfectly healthy, but the veins of the testicle and urinary organs were turgid with blood and varicose.

I COME next to consider the third species of malconformation of the heart, where the ductus arteriosus is obliterated, but the foramen ovale remains pervious, or a preternatural opening leads from the one ventricle to the other. These malconformations to produce bad effects, must be complicated with enlargement of the left side of the heart, or diminution of the calibre of the pulmonary artery.

WE very seldom find the foramen ovale and ductus arteriosus both open, but we very frequently observe the foramen ovale, pervious even in very advanced age, and this may proceed from two causes.

THE foramen ovale sometimes remains pervious, from a preternatural enlargement of the left side of the heart, whereby the blood still continues to pass from the right into the left side ; or it is occasionally kept open by a diminution of the size of the right ventricle and of the pulmonary artery.

IN the second place, this aperture may remain pervious from a total want of aptitude to unite, between the valve and the septum auriculæ ; or the same effect may take place from a partial adhesion only of these parts. Here we presume that all the cavities of the heart retain their healthy proportions to each other.

WITH regard to the foramen ovale, the ancients entertained mysterious notions, which some of the moderns have not yet dismissed from their systems : our forefathers saw the fœtus immersed in water for the space of nine months, and observed, that during the whole of this period, it did not respire. They were ignorant of the function of the placenta, they assigned to the foramen ovale an office which in reality belongs to the after-birth, and thus the doctrine of the use of the oval aperture gained currency, and was looked upon as an established fact in the animal œconomy. I cannot better illustrate the influence which some expect the foramen ovale to have upon the system, than by transcribing a paragraph from the transactions of the Royal Humane Society for the year 1803; where, among many other curious speculations of Dr. Hawes, we find the following, after pointing out the hurtful tendency of fear, when a person has been so unfortunate as to fall into the water; he observes, " that a firm habit, sobriety, " fortitude of mind, and a warm season, may " tend to protract life, and facilitate recovery;" all of which are intelligible facts, not so what follows: " If to these be added the foramen " ovale remaining open, (as in some instances " happens through life,) we may account why

" certain persons resist the watery element so
" much longer than others." This is only a small
part of what the foramen ovale was supposed
capable of performing. Many were the stories
recorded by the older Anatomists, respecting
the formation of divers and amphibious animals,
by keeping the foramen ovale open. Even so late
as the time of Buffon, this doctrine was in full
vigour, and so much was this celebrated natura-
list pleased with the conceit, that he clumsily
enough contrived a method for forming divers.
He even pleased himself with the belief, that he
had succeeded in his plan.

WITH regard to the effect of the foramen
ovale remaining open, I observe, that except in
those cases, where there is considerable difference of capacity of the right and left sides of
the heart, no very urgent symptoms originate
from the occurrence. When the left side is
much larger than the right, then indeed all the
symptoms of defective arterialization of the
blood, will be well marked and perfectly evident. I have seen one case where this conformation was productive of imperfect arterialization of the blood, marked by the usual phenomena; but I would wish you to understand,
that the disproportion between the sides of the
heart, is seldom so great as to produce this effect. Although this conformation be not in general competent to produce signs of a deficiency
of the arterial principle in the blood, yet it fre-

quently is productive of symptoms of asthma. This is a much overlooked cause of dyspnœa, but still it is one you will be very frequently called to remove; I have seen many examples of this species of asthma, and have ascertained, by dissection, the real cause of the symptoms. The mode by which it brings on the paroxysm, is very easily understood : the disproportion is not so great as to alter to a visible degree, the properties of the blood, but still it is sufficient to derange the harmony of action, between the heart and lungs. I have in the outset of this enquiry, stated that whatever affects the respiratory organs, influences the heart, and *vice versa.* Now we see, why in this formation, the disease, although seated in the heart, comes to put on the appearance of a morbid state of the lungs; we thus trace a gradation in the effects resulting from the foramen ovale remaining open, the symptoms being varied, and of greater or less urgency, according to the extent of the disparity between the sides of the heart. Preternatural openings in the septum of the auricle or ventricle, act in the same way; we have met with no examples of this malformation ourselves, but we find one detailed by that eminent and learned pathologist Dr. Hunter. The patient was a first born male child, remarkable from birth for ill health; he reached his thirteenth year, and was, we are informed, as tall as he ought to have been of his age; he was very thin, and yet did not seem to have been wasted by consumption. Dr. Hunter says " if a man had never seen any of the canine species, but the bull dog, he would be struck at the first sight of the slender and delicate Italian greyhound; this young gentleman's figure put me in mind of that animal, and when I looked upon him, I could not but think of the limbs of a wading water fowl."

HE from his earliest years was subject to fits, during which, his complexion, which had never been bright, became of a dusky hue, and in proportion as he grew up, the paroxysms were more frequent in their recurrence, and longer in their duration ; at last, he died during one of these fits.   Dr. Hunter examined the body, and found that at its origin, the pulmonary artery was very small, and that an opening of the size of the thumb led from the right into the left ventricle.

YOU will find in Morgagni's work, a case in some respects analogous to the one I have just related from Dr. Hunter.   It is that of a girl, who reached her sixteenth year, but who from her birth had been constantly weakly ; who had always more or less difficulty in breathing, and in whom there had never been a healthy colour of the skin, it had always been of a livid hue.

AFTER death it was discovered, that the heart was very small in proportion to the age of the subject, and that it was more obtuse than usual about the apex, which is, I believe often the

case in malformed hearts. The ventricles in regard to form and relative strength, seemed to
have changed places ; the right auricle was
twice as large and as thick in its sides as the
left, and the foramen ovale was so large as to
permit the little finger to pass from the one side
to the other; the valves defending the mouth of
the pulmonary artery, were at their floating extremities, cartilaginous, and even in one or two
spots ossified, and they were so connected with
each other, that only a small opening, not larger
than a barley seed, was left from the ventricle
into the artery; some small fleshy and membranous processes were attached to the edges of
the aperture.

ON this case I would observe, that the only difference between it, and that of the boy
recorded by Dr. Hunter, consists in the situation of the aperture leading from the right
to the left side of the heart. In the girl, the
foramen ovale remained pervious, whereas, in
the boy, an unnatural hole was found in the septum of the ventricles. In the symptoms produced, they nearly resembled each other. In Morgagni's patient you would also notice a circumstance, which I shall have occasion to recall to
your observation afterwards; I allude to the
thickening of the right auricle and ventricle.
You will from cases hereafter to be detailed,
learn, that when the blood is obstructed in its
passage, from any of the cavities of the heart

the muscularity of that cavity is for the most part augmented. This dissection affords a very good illustration of what takes place.

ON the fourth species of malconformation giving origin to imperfect arterialization of the blood, I have little to say, I have never seen an instance of it. Dr. Hunter once dissected a child, in whom the pulmonary artery was impervious at its origin: In this case, the symptoms of imperfect arterialization were very early and decidedly marked, and the disease terminated fatally on the 13th day. The body was dissected by Dr. H. the day after death. Respecting the morbid formation, he observes, " the great peculiarity of this case, was a pre-
" ternatural conformation of the pulmonary ar-
" tery, which at the beginning from the right
" ventricle, was contracted into a solid sub-
" stance or cord, and absolutely and complete-
" ly impervious, so that the lungs had not re-
" ceived one drop of blood from the heart, by
" the trunk of the pulmonary artery; the right
" ventricle therefore, had been of no use in trans-
" mitting the blood, and had scarcely any ca-
" vity left; the blood which was brought to the
" right auricle by the two cavæ and coronary
" veins, had passed through the foramen ovale,
" which was very large, into the left auricle,
" and so into the aorta, without passing through
" the lungs, and of course, without receiving
" the benefit of respiration. The pulmonary

" artery, except just at its origin, was every
" where pervious, though small; and the can-
" alis arteriosus had supplied it with a scanty
" share of blood, which was derived in a retro-
" grade way from the aorta. It was that small
" portion only of the blood, which had acquir-
" ed the good effects of air and breathing.

" I INJECTED the heart with plain suet after
" having carefully examined it, and when it had
" hardened by being kept in spirits some time,
" I opened both the auricle and ventricle of the
" right side, and picked out the suet to discover
" more exactly the state of these two cavities.

" THE canalis arteriosus in its course was
" very particular. Instead of going backwards
" as a continuation of the trunk of the pul-
" monary artery, it began from the left branch
" of that artery, rising upwards and forwards
" to its termination in the curvature of the
" aorta, nearly under or opposite to the left
" subclavian. It had carried the blood from
" the aorta to the pulmonary, and therefore
" took the appearance of a branch of the aorta,
" rather than that of the pulmonary artery.

" UPON opening the right ventricle, it ap-
" peared to be almost solid flesh, hardly any
" of the cavity having remained open. It was
" therefore very plain, that there had been no
" circulation of blood through the right ventri-
" cle. The returning blood of both cavæ, had
" passed through the foramen ovale, and left

" ventricle, into the aorta, from which by the
" canalis arteriosus a small portion had been
" conveyed by a retrograde motion into the
" left branch of the pulmonary artery, and
" thence, no doubt through the whole, to re-
" ceive the benefit of respiration."

THE next species of malconformation is very
rare; I know of only one case of it, described
by Mr. Wilson, teacher of anatomy in London.
In that instance, besides the malconformation,
there was also malposition, for the heart lay
in the abdomen. This *lusus* occurred in a child
seven days old, whose body was brought to the
theatre in Windmill-street, for dissection.

A MEMBRANOUS bag was distinctly perceived, reaching from the sternum to the umbilicus; on opening this, the heart was found contained within it, and imbedded in the substance
of the liver: Thus removed from the lungs, it
was necessary that its structure should be materially altered; it consisted of one auricle and
ventricle; from the ventricle, a large artery
arose and went up into the thorax; here it divided into two branches, one taking the usual
curvature of the aorta, and corresponding to it,
the other going to the lungs constituted the
pulmonary artery. From the lungs again, the
blood was returned by two veins, which joined
the vena cava superior, and entered the auricle
along with it; the lower cava was formed in the
usual way.

THIS heart in its formation, resembled the same organ in the class of Amphibiæ, and the blood was circulated in a similar manner.

THE sixth species of malconformation of the heart giving rise to an alteration in the state of the circulating fluids, is by no means of frequent occurrence. I have only seen three cases of this kind. In two of them, the mitral valve, instead of being formed of two flaps, presented only the appearance of a septum stretched across the opening from the auricle into the ventricle, having in the centre, an aperture of larger or smaller size, through which the blood passed from the one cavity into the other. In the first example which I saw of this kind, the patient was a slender male; subject to frequent cough, attended with profuse expectoration of mucus from the bronchi : He also complained of anxiety in the chest, and occasionally there was a tendency to a leaden colour of the surface; as we took no notes of the case, I cannot be more particular in the detail of the morbid phenomena, resulting from this conformation. When the person died, permission was procured to inspect the body. The lungs were found rather more solid than usual, and the mitral valve stretched directly across the foramen ventriculare, having only an oblong opening from the auricle into the ventricle, of about half an inch in the longest diameter. The margins of this aperture, were thick and cartilagenous, and farther out, some nodules of bone were formed in the valve. The morbid parts are preserved so as to illustrate clearly this morbid structure.

IN this patient, from the largeness of the opening, between the auricle and the ventricle, the blood was not so much impeded in its progress as in some of the other cases. The symptoms of imperfect arterialization, were not therefore so fully marked as in the two other cases, yet they were sufficiently obvious to call attention to that circumstance. They were not however so urgent as they are sometimes met with in people who have merely mechanical obstruction, to the respiratory function. In this species of morbid formation, as the blood does not pass freely from the left auricle into the ventricle, it is evident that the circulation through the lungs must be impeded, and that on using exertion, or otherwise hurrying the circulation, the blood must in a greater or less degree accumulate in the pulmonary vessels, compressing the bronchial cells, and thus occasioning in some degree, the symptoms of a deficiency of the arterial principle in the blood. From this view of the matter, it is evident, that this malconformation produces its bad effects, by preventing the arterialization of the blood, and not as in the former instances, by intermixing the venous with the arterial blood. In this respect therefore, this malconformation produces its bad effects in the same way as tumors pressing on the lungs. We shall afterwards see that this structure may also be a cause of hæmorrhage from the lungs. In general those who have this malconformation of the mitral valve, die dropsical, and in two of the three I have seen, the right side of the heart was considerably enlarged.

THE second case occurred in the year 1802. It was that of Elizabeth Brown, aged 19 years, who from birth had been extremely delicate, subject to pectoral complaints, syncope and darkness of the surface, and who during the last two years of her life, had been much troubled with irregular action of the heart, and dropsical symptoms. At last, fluid was accumulated in the abdomen, in such quantity as to threaten rupture of its sides. At this stage of her illness, she complained frequently, but more especially after using exertion, of a disagreeable throbbing sensation in the epigastric region. By examining this part, while the abdomen was tense, a slight undulating motion could only be felt, but after the fluid had been removed by the operation of paracentesis, the throbbing in the epigastrium was very remarkable. By the violence of the pulsation, the integuments were alternately elevated and depressed to a very considerable extent, and by placing the hand over the pit of the stomach, a tumor was felt in the upper part of the belly, synchronous in its action with the heart. She complained more of the working of this swelling than of any other symptom, and toward the latter part of her life, the uneasiness resulting from this, increased rather than diminished. After having had the operation of paracentesis performed six times, she died without any material alteration in the affection of the heart.

As soon as we heard that the girl was dead, we solicited permission to inspect the body, which was very readily granted at the request of Dr. Cleghorn, lecturer on chemistry in this University, under whose care the patient had been placed previous to her death. This was done by Dr. Baird, Dr. Pollock, and myself.

On opening the thorax, we found a quantity of serum in the cavity of the chest, and also in the pericardium; but it did not in either exceed a very few ounces. Notwithstanding the trifling quantity of fluid it contained, the pericardium was enormously distended. It occupied all the arterior part of the thorax, and extended considerably into the epigastric region, pushing before it the diaphragm. When the heart was fairly exposed, by slitting open the pericardium, we found it very unequally dilated. The right side was immensely enlarged, while the left was rather smaller than usual. The right auricle was fully as large as a child's head of a year old, and filled with clots of blood. The corresponding ventricle seemed rather less; the venæ cavæ were much dilated; the inferior admitted with ease four fingers; the foramen ventriculare equalled in size the inferior cava, and the tricuspidal valve was rigid, and in some places ossified. The valves at the origin of the pulmonary artery were healthy, and the vessel itself seemed of its usual capacity.

THE left auricle was extremely small, but its structure was apparently healthy, the ventricle was also small, but proportionally thicker and stronger than usual. From the annulus ventricularis a tendinous septum was stretched over the opening leading from the auricle into the ventricle. This septum was rigid, and in some spots ossified; it was perforated at the centre by a puckered aperture, of a size just sufficient to admit the tip of the little finger. It might aptly enough be compared to the iris perforated by the pupil. Nearer the cavity of the ventricle than the curtain, the mitral valves arose as usual from the annulus ventricularis. The flaps were stiff, and in some spots loaded with calcareous matter. The columnæ carneæ and cordæ tendineæ, were healthy. The aorta at its origin and through its whole course, was exceedingly small. Its size was not at any part larger than that of the little finger, and the trunks sent off from it were, if possible, still more diminutive. I need not specify the measurements of the individual trunks, the external iliac vessel, was about the size of a goose quill, and the rest in proportion.

AFTER stating the particulars of this case, I would only observe, that, in this girl, as the opening from the auricle into the ventricle, was considerably smaller than in the former instance, so were the symptoms arising from defective arterialization of the blood more urgent. We have also seen from the dissection, that the left side of the heart and the whole of the arterial system, were altogether out of proportion to the other parts of the body. This peculiar reduction of the size of the left side of the heart, and the curious formation of the opening from the auricle into the ventricle, will sufficiently account for the state of the pulse, which was frequent, fluttering, and often intermittent. But whether the state of the arterial system will explain the great dilatation of the right side, is a question which will come to be considered afterwards.

THIS case also illustrates another fact, which is highly worthy of being known to every practitioner. It shews that all the symptoms of aneurism of one of the abdominal vessels, may exist where there is no organic affection of any of the vessels. There is reason to believe, that in this girl, the pulsation in the epigastrium, was in part occasioned by the dilated ventricle and auricle impelling forward the liver; and it would also, in some measure, appear to have depended on the reflux of the blood from the enlarged auricle, into the veins of the liver.

Whether we admit these conjectures as a proper explanation of the phenomenon or not, still a knowledge of the fact may assist us materially in forming a diagnosis in similar cases.

ALTHOUGH it does not properly make a part of the history of this case, I may observe, that in all the six operations for the removal of the fluid from the belly, the perforation was made midway between the spine of the ilium and the umbilicus; and also, that in each the trocar was entered within the eighth part of an inch, from where it had formerly passed. In the four first operations, the fluid was very readily removed without the effusion of any blood, but in removing the water the fifth time, it was found tinged with blood, and when the canula was withdrawn, a stream of venous blood issued from the wound. The farther effusion of blood was prevented by the eighteen tailed bandage. On inspecting the body after death, it was found that the stilet had punctured the enlarged ascending branch of the vena circumflexa ilü. I mention this, for the purpose of observing, that in performing the operation of paracentesis at this point, an obstinate hemorrhage has occurred to many surgeons, and this has uniformly been conjectured to have arisen from injury of the epigastric artery. If, however, the epigastric vessel has ever been injured in this operation, it must have run in a very unusual course. I think it more probable, that in most of them, the instrument had divided the ascending branch of the circumflex artery. It is often as large nearly as the epigastric, and it always lies precisely in the line of operation.

THE last case I shall mention, is that of a young man who had for a considerable length of time, been under the care of Dr. Balmanno; I need not enter into a detailed account of the symptoms, for *mutatis mutandis*, I should have almost to transcribe the case of E. B. The patient was subject to dropsical affections, and his surface was of a dusky colour; he had, toward the latter period of his life, occasional hemorrhage from the lungs. The general languor, and the state of the pulse, however, shewed that this hemorrhage was produced not from over-action of the sanguiferous system, but from the state of the pulmonary circulation.

THE body was examined by Dr. Balmanno, and Dr. Brown. It was found that the right side of the heart was enormously dilated, but it was healthy in its structure. The left side was rather larger than natural, the auricle was much ossified, and its inner surface was coated over with an incrustation, similar to that which is met with in aneurismal tumors; and it also contained a large solid concretion of lymphatic matter intermixed with specks of bone, which adhered with considerable force to the side of the auricle. In place of the regular structure of the mitral valve, there was an aponeurotic

expansion stretched across the foramen ventriculare: This curtain about its middle was
perforated by a small chink, hardly large enough
to admit the tip of the little finger.   The edges
of the hole were tumid and stiff, and into the
lower surface of the septum, the cordæ ten-
dinosæ were fixed.   They were not however
attached to the margin only of the aperture,
but on the contrary, were implanted at irregular distances along the whole extent of the curtain, so that when they were pulled, this curtain
was rendered slightly concave toward the auricle, and convex toward the ventricle.   The
structure of the ventricle was healthy, and the
aorta did not appear smaller than usual.

THROUGH the kindness of Dr. Balmanno, who
is zealously interested in the prosecution of
morbid anatomy, I have been put in possession
of the preparation of these parts, as well as of
many other specimens illustrative of diseased
structure.

AFTER these observations were written, I was
favoured by my friend Dr. Brown, lecturer on bo-
tany in the University of Glasgow, with the history of the following case, which occurred while
he was house-surgeon in the Edinburgh hospital.
As the case illustrates the same points which
have been already insisted on, I shall make no
apology for its insertion. It, along with the other
cases, which have just been described, of malconformation of the mitral valve, shews that

the patients are generally carried off while
young.

" JANUARY 30th, Christie Howard, aged thir-
" teen was admitted into the hospital, affected
" with dyspnœa, and frequent palpitations of
" the heart on exercise. During the palpita-
" tion, the beating of the heart was felt between
" the 6th and 7th rib, and conveyed a jarring
" sensation to the hand ; the pulse was 80,
" small and sharp, her legs were œdematous,
" her lips livid, and she was very feeble, and
" frequently drowsy. Her complaints were of
" a year and a half's duration ; she had taken
" digitalis with apparent relief, and had an open
" blister on her breast. A few cordials were
" occasionally administered ; all other medi-
" cines were discontinued, and she was dismis-
" sed about the 19th of March, relieved.

" SHE returned to the hospital in the month
" of May following, affected with general drop-
" sy, and after using many medicines without
" sensible relief, she died in the month of June.

" ON dissection about two pounds of serum
" were found in the cavities of the thorax, and
" about five ounces in the pericardium. The
" right ventricle of the heart was thickened.
" The mitral valve had lost the appearance of
" a valve, was constricted and thickened, so as
" to form a firm ring with a hole in the mid-
" dle, about the size of a goose quill ; the aorta
" was a good deal inflamed ; there was a con-

" siderable quantity of serum in the abdomen ;
" the liver was sound, but a little paler than
" usual."

ALL these cases shew, that the state of the
opening from the auricle into the ventricle is
one, which from the time of birth till the period
of death, is productive of incessant uneasiness,
and eventually of death. It is productive of a
disease, which, for a time may be palliated, but
which cannot be cured.

I HAVE thus finished the observations, which
I had to offer on the causes and consequences
of imperfect arterialization of the blood ; these
causes you have seen to consist in a radical defect in the formation of either the heart or large
arteries; a defect, which it is beyond the power
of medicine to remove. To attempt therefore,
to cure this disease, is futile. As I have
already stated, we are in most diseases of the
heart, called upon rather to prevent positive
evil, than to remove what already is present;
and the means to be employed in palliation of
this complaint, I have already pointed out.

THE Third class of diseases of the Heart,
comprehends those affections in which none of
the symptoms characterising a deficiency in the
blood of the arterial principle are necessarily
present. These diseases are often dependent
upon an organic affec on of the heart, which
mechanica ly impairs the circulation, and from
the frequency and fatality of many of them,

it is highly requisite that the practitioner should know their nature and symptoms, as far as these can be explained in the present imperfect state of our acquaintance with this class of morbid affections.

OBSERVATIONS

ON UNIFORM ENLARGEMENT, AND ON DILATATION OF THE HEART.

DILATATION, either general or partial, is one of the most frequent, and at the same time, one of the simplest diseases to which the heart is subjected. Frequent however as dilatation is, and easily as it is discovered by dissection, it does not appear that it had been distinctly noticed before the time of the illustrious Vesalius. No age nor sex would seem to be exempt from this affection, yet it appears more frequently among those advanced in years, than in young people. It is difficult to ascertain by dissection many of the diseased conditions of the heart, but dilatation is apparent even to a superficial observer. In general, the human heart does not weigh above a few ounces, but by disease, its weight is sometimes enormously increased,

Lieutaud describes a heart which weighed five
pounds, and others even speak of having found
it heavier.   It is not however to be imagined
that in every instance where the heart is larger
than usual, the symptoms will be such as are
dependent on increased size of its cavities.   In
nature it is much the reverse: sometimes this
organ is apparently very large, and yet we find
that its cavities are very small.   This takes
place when the heart is enlarged by an addition
of solid substance, not only cellular but even
muscular.   I have seen a heart which weighed
several pounds, in which the cavities were not
more capacious than usual.   To those, however,
who like the old physiologists, ascribe all the
movements of the arterial system, to the impulse communicated to the blood by the fibres
of the heart, this conformation will appear, if not
absolutely advantageous, at least, not hurtful.
But who has attended to the reciprocal action of the heart and arteries, or who has ever
seen an example of this disease, and is not
convinced that such a state is highly dangerous? The balance between the heart and arteries is lost.   By the great addition of muscular
substance, the whole sanguiferous system is
thrown into a deranged state of action, and by
the encroachment of the distended pericardium
on the cavity of the chest, a greater or less
effect is produced on the lungs.   There is a
confusion and a struggling in the chest, there is

also an inexpressible anxiety and inquietude about the heart; and, as one would expect, there " is a weak, irregular, intermitting, fluttering " pulse ;" or, as in a case of this disease recorded by Valsalva, the pulse is rapid and corded. But I cannot conceive what has induced Mr. Bell, Dr. Ferrier, and Portal, to lay these down as the symptoms attendant on dilatation of the cavities of the heart. They are the symptoms which belong to enlargement of the solid substance of this organ; or to dilatation of the cavities combined with chronic inflammation and adhesion of the pericardium, conditions which cannot be too carefully distinguished from the other. Both are without doubt dangerous, but they are not equally dangerous. The solid increase is a deplorable affection, one hardly admitting of palliation, one which exhausts the bodily strength, and overpowers the faculties of the mind, ruining every source of enjoyment, and distressing the patient with never ceasing feelings of instantaneous dissolution. But as we shall by and by see, in simple dilatation of the cavities of the heart, the case is by no means so desperate, for here the disease is insidious, and has often reached to a great extent before the symptoms became urgent; and even in the close of this affection, the sensations are far more supportable and the issue more consolatory than in the former disease. In the simple dilatation of the cavities, I have never seen symptoms such

as those described by Dr. Ferrier, who says,
" That the most certain sign of dilatation is
" the jarring sensation given to the hand by
" each systole. The stroke seems restrained,
" and is succeeded by a kind of thrilling,
" which cannot clearly be described, but is en-
" tirely different from the stroke of a palpi-
" tation :" And again, " The pulse is very
" irregular, sometimes feeble, small, and inter-
" mitting, sometimes extremely quick, and
" hard, or jarring like the systole of the heart
" itself." These, as I have already said, are the
symptoms occasioned either by a solid increase
of the size of the heart, by dilatation of its cavities complicated with chronic inflammation,
or by uniform dilatation, complicated with a
considerable reduction of the size of the arterial
system ; and these are, I suspect, the cases from
which Portal has also described the symptoms
of dilatation. In the cases of genuine unmixed
dilatation which I have seen, the symptoms
have been quite the reverse ; the patients have
complained of an oppression in the chest, of a
sense of occasional suffocation ; the pulse has
uniformly been full, slow, and soft, even in one
instance beating so low, as eleven pulsations in
the course of a minute. The heart has been
felt contracting sluggishly, and equally in the
chest. There have been dropsical symptoms
blended with a stomachic ailment, and with
torpidity of the bowels. It is very rare to see

a case of dilatation proceed to a fatal termination, without the accession of chronic inflammation ; and if this once commence, the whole complexion of the disease is changed, and the symptoms as described by authors are induced. Where chronic inflammation does not supervene, dropsy of the pericardium often comes on. This renders the enlargement to a superficial observer, much more apparent than real. Frequently, where the pulsation is felt even so low as the eleventh rib, the heart in reality is little affected. We may judge of the existence of serous effusion into the pericardium by the sensation, as if a bag of water were felt interposed between the heart and the hand, and also by feeling when the patient is leaning forward, and inclining rather to the left side, an obscure pulsation low in the chest, and a more forcible beat in the position of the heart. Likewise in a case treated by Dr. Ferrier, neither the pulses at the wrists were synchronous, nor the pulse in either wrist, with the systole of the heart. In a patient seen by Valsalva, the dilated heart and dropsical pericardium, so affected the pulse, that it was rendered almost imperceptible; and some practical writers assure us, that a remarkable slowness of the pulse may almost be considered as pathognomonic of dropsy of the pericardium ; but with regard to this, when not complicated with dilatation of the heart, I can say nothing from experience.

CONCERNING the causes of this disease, we
are very much in the dark. If we apply to
authors for information on this head, we find
abundance of conjectures respecting the influence of acrimony.   " Les humeurs acri-
" monieuses peuvent aussi affecter le cœur,
" et en relacher le tissu, de maniere que les
" parois ne pouvant ensuite resister a l'effort
" du sang, se dilatent plus ou moins." This
vague conjecture is delivered with great gra-
vity by the venerable Portal, in his late work
on Anatomy.   Some again discarding the
agency of acrimonious juices, ascribe the dilatation to a reduction of the capacity of the arterial system; while others that they might
have a theory of their own, assure us, that the
dilatation of the heart is not dependent on the
smallness of the aorta, but that the artery is
reduced in size, because the overloaded heart
cannot disgorge itself; and in individual cases,
these discordances are seemingly supported by
observation, the heart being sometimes found of
enormous magnitude, while the arterial system
is small and *vice versa*.   It would be a waste of
time to attempt to refute the various supposi-
tions of authors on this subject ; suffice it to say,
that in general, the dilatation is not accomplished by any mechanical agent.   We know that in-
dividuals are predisposed to peculiar diseases, and
that these different affections are produced by similar exciting causes.   The heart may, and of-

ten does receive a tendency to dilatation, from obstruction to the transmission of the blood from the one cavity of the heart into another, or from the heart into the large vessels. But I cannot believe that this stoppage of the passage of the blood can effect mechanically, any augmentation of the size of the heart. This organ dilates as much, independent of distension, as the uterus does in extra uterine gestation, or even in common pregnancy. Dilatation of the heart, and enlargement of the gravid womb, are perfectly analogous, only in the one case, the increase of size tends to a useful purpose, whereas in the other, it is *ab origine* morbid. From a review of the cases of dilatation contained in Lieutaud's work, you will see that many of them were complicated with diseased valves, by which the passage of the blood would be obstructed; and by recurring to the cases which have been already described, you will perceive that malconformation of the mitral valve, is often accompanied with dilatation of the heart. But it must have struck you, that as in two of these cases, the malconformation was an original structure, the right side of the heart, must in these people have preponderated in size, even from the cradle to the grave. There are many examples on record of partial dilatation of the heart, complicated with diseased valves, but from what we have seen, we cannot conclude with Dr. Parry, " that in almost every instance

" where any discrimination is made in the de-
" scription, that side or even that cavity of the
" heart, which in the course of circulation was
" nearest, before the obstructed part, is said to
" have suffered the greatest degree of dilata-
" tion." In some cases which have come to
my knowledge, where the mitral valve was diseased, the right ventricle has not been much
dilated, but has been much thickened; while
the right auricle was enormously dilated, and
the left auricle of the natural size, but also thickened. The explanation of these cases will come
more properly to be noticed when treating of
ossification of the valves.

HAVING premised these general observations
on the history of dilatation of the heart, I may
now illustrate the disease, by the detail of a
case, which came under the care of Mr. Jamieson, surgeon in Glasgow. A man aged forty,
began without any obvious cause to complain
of anxiety and oppression in the chest, accompanied with a constant disposition to syncope, upon using even trivial exertion. The
paroxysms of breathlessness were frequent, and
the pulse fell from its usual standard, (70 to 80):
at first to 18, then to 12, and in the end it was
so low as 11 and 10 beats in the course of a
minute. The pulse did not give the sensation
described by authors, but on the contrary was full
and soft. The feet became œdematous, and on
laying the hand over the chest, a sluggish stroke

was felt in the region of the heart, and diffused over almost the whole extent of the thorax. In this situation he remained for several years, and on the day preceding his death, he had not been worse than usual, although considerably fatigued by walking slowly a mile. Notwithstanding his fatigue, he supped heartily, went to bed, and had slept about two hours, when he suddenly awaked convulsed, and almost instantly expired. Before his wife, who was alarmed by his struggles, could procure assistance, he was dead.

As the case was one of considerable interest, Mr. Jamieson found little difficulty in persuading the relations to allow the body to be examined. When the thorax was laid open, the immense bag formed by the dilated pericardium, could alone at first be seen; by slitting up this capsule, the heart was brought into view, occupying the anterior and lateral parts of the chest, distended with dark coagulated blood, and loaded with fat. It was an unseemly mass, its huge auricles and broad ventricles were longer than those of an ox, and the vessels passing out from it were healthy in their structure, but rather larger than usual. All the cavities were equally dilated, and the auricles, ventricles, and vessels, were of the same thickness as they ought to have been, had the heart not been dilated.

AFTER the heart had been removed from the body, and cleaned from the pericardium, lungs and fat, it weighed two pounds.

THIS case establishes as clearly as a single case can, the fallacy of the description usually given of the symptoms accompanying dilatation of the heart, and from the measurement and weight of this heart, compared with those of the hearts spoken of by some writers, I think, I am authorised to say, that the cases in general, related as having been simple dilatation, have been those in which this affection was blended either with enlargement of the solid substance of this organ, or in which chronic inflammation had been present. That this is a correct supposition, I think I shall be able to prove, for we have met with a case in which the simple dilatation proceeded for a considerable length, and then the chronic inflammation took place. This case shall be described when contrasting simple dilatation, with dilatation combined with chronic inflammation. Simple dilatation is a chronic affection, the symptoms seldom bearing any proportion to the extent of the disease. In most people, until the complaint is pretty far advanced, the functions are performed with tolerable regularity. In this case, the person during six years, had decided marks of dilated heart, and yet during all that time, he had been able to go about; and his wife, a woman of respectable character, had born several children, and at the period of his death, was advanced to the seventh month of utero gestation. Here the fatal termination seemed to be produced by the slow encroachment of the heart on the cavity of the chest, and also by the insidious loss of tone of its flabby fibres. In other instances, however, death has undoubtedly been caused by rupture of the heart itself; but, on the whole, we more frequently in dilatation of this organ, find the patient carried off by the accession of chronic inflammation.

I HAVE just related a case where the heart was uniformly dilated, and in which the vessels were also increased in size; and from this history, to which I could add another nearly similar, from my own preparations, you will at once perceive, that where both the heart and arteries are dilated, the pulse is in the state I have described. In the eighteenth letter and second article of Morgagni's epistles, you will read a case, where the heart was monstrously dilated, and the aorta contracted; and in this patient there was dyspnœa, a tendency to syncope, with an unequal pulse; and toward the close of life, a pain in the situation of the diaphragm, a cough and a languid frequent pulse, and vomiting of greenish matter appeared a short time before death.

THE heart was larger than if two healthy hearts were joined, and all its cavities were dilated; but what struck Morgagni most forcibly, was the small size of the aorta. The person had been a strong male, yet the " aorta was more suitable to a little woman, than to a man who was like him rather of a large stature." This history I would wish you to consider as a valuable addition, for it shews most clearly, the difference between a dilated heart, accompanied with dilatation of the trunk of the arterial system, and one which is complicated with a contracted state of the arteries. It corroborates the general statement, and will convince you how necessary it is to record, not only the condition of the heart, but also of the vascular system, for the state of the latter has considerable influence in modifying the symptoms. I could, to illustrate this point, bring forward other cases, but one from so respectable an authority as Morgagni, I consider sufficient.

OBSERVATIONS

ON PARTIAL DILATATION OF THE HEART.

UNIFORM dilatation of the cavities of the heart, such as we have been considering, is of rare occurrence; more frequently, the one side is more affected than the other, and the right side more frequently dilated than the left; sometimes the left side is of its usual magnitude, while the right is as large as that of the heart of an ox, and yet from this great disproportion in the relative capacity of the two sides of the heart, little inconvenience, comparatively speaking, is felt. From abstract reasoning on the consequences of this disease, we would naturally expect to find the symptoms more urgent, than when both sides of the heart, and the vascular system were equally dilated. Experience proves the very reverse, for we often see the right side of the heart, enormously dilated, where the symptoms have been very moderate, and it is worthy of observation, that we generally, in a case of this kind, have it in our power to moderate the progress of the disease.

SOME assure us, that when the right auricle and ventricle are alone affected, the pulsation in the chest is obscure, deep seated, and spreads rather across the thorax, than in any other direction; is accompanied with sense of weight in the breast, and pulsation in the veins of the neck. I have met with many cases of this partial dilatation, and have generally found, that except when the patients had been overexerting themselves, or exciting the vascular system, by drinking ardent spirits, the symptoms were hardly even troublesome. The difficulty of breathing was slightly complained of, and some were affected with cough and spitting of blood. Indeed, in those who have the right side of the heart much dilated, it is astonishing to find the animal functions carried on. Seeing, on examining bodies, the one side so much larger than the other, I have often wondered, how

the bad effects which we would naturally expect to have resulted from such a state, have
been obviated. In health, we shall suppose,
that the right auricle is capable of containing
only two ounces of blood; the corresponding
ventricle the same quantity, and the pulmonary
artery no more. When, however, the heart is dilated, these just relations are lost, the balance
between the heart and vessels being destroyed.
We shall take it for granted, that the auricle
and ventricle are each of them dilated so far, as
easily to contain three ounces of fluid, but that
the pulmonary artery remains of its usual size.
If the ventricle propels the whole of this blood,
the consequence must be terrible, the ultimate
branches of this vessel in the lungs will give
way; the blood then finding a road into the bronchiæ, will obstruct the passage of the air, de-
prive the blood of its oxygen, and finally kill
the patient. Now this is a description most
scrupulously correct, and if it uniformly took
place in every case, in which the right ventricle
was enlarged, we should have little inducement
to study this complaint. Fortunately, however,
this does not hold; it occurs only under particular circumstances, for the ventricles accommo-
date, even in a dilated heart, the quantity of
fluid they propel, to the capacity of the vessel
which is to receive it. But although I have
mentioned, that the cavities of the heart only
propel as much blood as the vessels are fitted

easily to receive, it is to be understood, that
this accommodating property in dilatation of
the heart is restricted, and is only effectual
while this organ is acting slowly. If we accelerate the action of the heart, beyond a certain
extent, the ventricle instead of adapting the
quantity of blood it sends out, to the capacity
of the pulmonary artery, contracts completely;
and consequently expels more than a proper
quantity of its contents; the pulmonic vessels
by the congestion and continued *vis a tergo* are
ruptured; blood is forced into the air cells;
hymoptysis is produced; or if urged still further,
all the cellular structure of the lungs is crammed with blood; these organs cut like liver, and
sink when put into water. This I am convinced from repeated observation, is a frequent
cause of hæmorrhage from the lungs, and I have
seen several, who have lost their lives, from not
preserving the vascular action within proper limits. The first case I had an opportunity of
seeing of this kind, occurred about eight years
ago, and the connection between the over-action
of the heart and arteries, and the bleeding from
the lungs, was too obvious to escape notice.
The person was a stout well made man, but a
notorious drunkard; healthy till the latter part
of his life, when he began on using exertion, or
otherwise accelerating the vascular system, to
complain of uneasiness in the thorax, accompanied with apparent difficulty in breathing, with

coughing, and occasional spitting of blood. Although he was convinced from repeated observation, that inebriety exasperated his ailments, still
he was intoxicated as often as his means would
permit. By these irregularities his condition
became worse and worse; the fits of coughing,
and expectoration of blood, returned more frequently; and at last during complete intoxication, a violent paroxysm of coughing came on,
a torrent of blood issued from the lungs, and he
died from suffocation. From the constant discharge of blood from the lungs, when the vascular system was excited to increased action,
we were led to suspect that the disease was
seated in the heart. We requested and obtained permission to inspect the body, and found
that our conjectures were well founded. Both
auricle and ventricle, of the right side of the
heart, were much enlarged, and were crammed
with grumous blood; the pulmonary artery
was also filled with coagulated blood, and the
lungs were almost solid; the pleura pulmonalis
was raised from the substance of the lungs, by
the effused blood; and the trachea contained
shreds of bloody lymph mixed with air. From
the appearances presented by the dissection of
this person, compared with the previous symptoms, there could be no doubt of a connection
having subsisted between the enlargement of
the right side of the heart, and the discharge
of blood from the trachea, whenever the san-

guiferous system was excited to more than natural action. Since then, I have seen the
same repeatedly exemplified, in similar diseased conditions of the heart; and indeed by
almost every author, on enlargement of this
organ, it is stated, that occasionally, blood
flows from the aspera arteria. No writer, however, that I know, has sufficiently investigated
the nature and causes of this bloody discharge,
and no one has duly enforced the necessity of
restraining the vascular action. Stimuli in such
a case, must be carefully avoided, and above
all, the person must refrain from the use of ardent spirits. Their abuse is in general speedily
fatal, for they destroy the power of accommodation, which in a heart so formed, is the very an-
chor of hope, of the patient.

IN some cases it has been found, that the
right side of the heart had its solid substance
greatly increased, while the left was enormously dilated. A history of the symptoms produced by this condition of the heart, will be found
in Morgagni's work. This author relates, that,
the patient was a poor man, sixty-five years
of age, who for several years, had been subject
to oppression in the chest, accompanied with
dyspnœa, and tendency to syncope, and a slow
tense and cord-like pulse. When he had continued for several years in this state, he was attacked with intermittent fever, which by the
use of proper remedies, began to abate in the

severity and frequency of its paroxysms. But as the fever decreased, the feeling of constriction in the chest, and irregular action of the heart increased, so that, on the eleventh day after his admission into the hospital, he seemed to be *in articulo mortis;* yet he did not die till about the fortieth day of his illness. On the twentieth day, he was very much reduced; and on the twenty-seventh, he complained of a sensation of a most oppressive fulness in the chest, which continued till the thirtieth, when the pulse became almost natural, and he expectorated a quantity of gelatinous matter, mixed with a pale brown substance. His death was accelerated by the accession of gangrene about the buttocks.

THE body was opened by Albertini, who found the lungs adhering to the pleura, and of a dark colour; the pericardium contained about a pound and a half of yellowish black serum, and the heart was as large as that of an ox; the cavity of the right ventricle was of healthy size, but its muscular substance was much thickened on the left side; the ventricle was so much dilated as to be capable of containing within it another heart, and its sides were very thin; the aorta was enlarged in proportion to the heart, and its inner coats had assumed a cartilaginous texture.

THIS case, whether we consider the symptoms which preceded death, or the appearances discovered by dissection, is exceedingly curious.

From the state of the right ventricle, we would have been led to expect irregular action of the pulmonary artery, and perhaps bloody expectoration; but the state of the pulse is almost incredible. In the beginning of the complaint, it was slow, tense, and cord-like which you will easily understand: But how in the decline of life, it could rise to its natural standard, when the left ventricle of the heart was weakened, and the aorta was cartilaginous, is difficult to conceive.

ENLARGEMENT of the heart, whether general or partial, is an affection which we cannot cure. But by proper remedies and attention to diet, and the state of the stomach and bowels, we may palliate symptoms, and keep for a length of time the patient in a tolerable easy state. From the great tendency of this disease to terminate in chronic inflammation, we are to use our endeavours to prevent the accession of this new morbid condition, which rarely fails to carry off the patient in a very few days. I know no remedy better adapted for the purpose, than a seton introduced over the situation of the heart; we employ the seton not for the purpose of removing inflammatory action, but to prevent its occurrence; with a similar view we occasionally prescribe digitalis. I do not intend to say, how this medicine acts, but I can from observation declare, that it has a very powerful effect in obviating the urgency of the symptoms

in dilatation of the heart; and I can safely recommend its employment in aneurism of the
arch of the aorta. As the dilatation of the heart
is very often complicated with dropsical symptoms, we must have recourse to the employment of diuretics; and as the stomach and
bowels never fail to be deranged, we must prescribe laxatives joined with carminatives. If
the patient keeps quiet, and submits to regular
diet, light and digestible, and employs occasional remedies to obviate the dyspeptic symptoms, it affords him comfort to know, that he
may ward off the fatal issue, for a considerable
length of time, and may even enjoy tolerable
health, during the progress of the dilatation.

OBSERVATIONS

ON CHRONIC INFLAMMATION OF THE HEART.

VERY frequently, dilatation of the heart is
complicated with chronic inflammation and adhesion of the pericardium, to the surface of the
heart, by which the symptoms are much modified, and the whole complexion of the disease
altered. In this disease, the pulse is always frequent, irregular, and jarring, the reverse of what
takes place in simple dilatation, where it is
slow, full, and extremely sluggish; and also

in the former disease, a curious circumstance occurs; the enlargement appears to go on with extreme rapidity, is uniformly accompanied with a febrile affection, and generally an acute pain is felt in the abdomen. As none of these symptoms are ever attendant on unmixed dilatation, their presence is to be considered as pathognomonic of this complicated disease. The pain is often seated in the hypogastrium, and I have even found it accompanied with actual suppression of the urine, and that, in a case where dissection shewed, there was no organic affection of the urinary organs themselves. Frequently likewise, the pain is referred to the epigastrium, where there is often an evident pulsation felt; but this pulsation in the epigastrium, is rarely perceived till the disease be pretty far advanced. The pulsation is frequently so conspicuous, as to give rise to a supposition of the patient having aneurism of the coeliac artery. I have been often misled, and have seen others of more ability deceived; indeed, it so often happens, that reputed cases of coeliac aneurism, originate from some other disease, altogether unconnected with that vessel; that, when I now meet with a person having a pulsation in the epigastrium, I almost uniformly decide in my own mind, that the coeliac artery is healthy. I have met with above twenty instances of pulsating tumors in the region of the coeliac artery, and many of these were by myself and others, supposed to be coeliac aneurism; and yet it turned out on dissection, that not one of all of them had originated from a diseased state of that, or any other artery. In the only case of aneurism of the coeliac artery I ever saw, and which I had an opportunity of examining, through the friendship of Mr. Russel, the person was not suspected to have any disease, far less so serious a one, as that of which she died. Her relations and the byestanders, were shocked to see her instantaneously expire, with racking pain at the pit of the stomach, brought on by the action of an emetic, which they had officiously recommended to remove a degree of nausea and weight, which she felt about the stomach. In this instance, where the tumor was as large as the fist, and where it had burst and forced its blood up along the outer surface of the œsophagus, into the chest, to the amount of eight or ten pounds; the pulsation was so obscure, that it passed unnoticed. Not so, however, in that species of pulsating tumor produced by disease of the heart; there, the tumor is firm, and the throbbing furious; and the practitioner, unless much on his guard, may be easily deceived. From what I have been able to collect, from those who have seen cases of real coeliac aneurism, it would appear, that the pulsation is obscure and deep seated; but in that species of pulsation, dependent on disease of the heart, the beating of the tumor is superficial, defined, and distinct. Various causes give rise to this beating tumor in the epigastric region, but the most frequent source is from adhesion of the pericardium to the surface of the heart. This union of the pericardium and the heart, must uniformly give rise to pulsation in the epigastrium. To understand how this is produced, we must attend to the influence of these on each other, during a state of health. Some physiologists are of opinion, that the heart, when it contracts, becomes smaller than the pericardium. This, however, is a mistaken idea, for, in fact, the heart is always embraced by its capsule, as well, during the contraction, as during its relaxation. All the parts of the heart do not act at the same moment; if they did, then a vacuity must, during its contraction, have been left between its outer surface and the pericardium. On the contrary, the two auricles act in concert; and in an exact proportion as they contract, the ventricles dilate, and *vice versa*. The auricles and the ventricles, therefore, balance each other, and the only effect produced, is, that the surface of the heart brushes along the inner surface of the pericardium, in the same way that the pleura pulmonalis glides over the pleura costalis, during the motions of respiration. In the alternate contraction and dilatation of the auricles and ventricles, the pericardium is completely quiescent, it is uniformly of the same size, and it supports the heart in all its movements. When the pericardium adheres to the heart, then in proportion to the extent of the adhesion, so will this organ be curbed in its motions; for now, the surface of the heart can no longer glide along that of the pericardium, and the latter, cannot be easily made to move along with the heart, for it is pretty firmly fixed to the neighbouring parts, and hangs suspended between the sternum, the spine, and the diaphragm. Any change which now takes place in the capacity of the heart, must be accompanied with a displacement of the diaphragm; this septum must be elevated and depressed alternatively, during the contraction and dilatation of the heart. By this alternate raising and depressing of the diaphragm, the repercussions of the heart affect the liver; producing thus, a pulsating tumor *in epigastrio*, which almost invariably, in every case of chronic inflammation of the heart, is attended with adhesion of the pericardium, and more especially, if the right side of the heart be at the same time dilated, forms the most unpleasant feature in the complaint.

IN chronic inflammation of the heart, if the hand be applied over the chest, a very unpleasant sensation is communicated to it. There is a feeling as if some water was interposed between the heart and the hand, and that, even where not a single drop of fluid is contained in the chest or pericardium. As the disease proceeds, the breathing becomes more and more laborious and difficult, the face becomes bloated, the limbs adematous, water collects in the abdomen, and in a few days, or at most, weeks, the patient dies. Often, as Dr. Ferrier observes, the patient complains of a violent beating in the head.

ON examining the bodies of those who have died from this disease, very little derangement will be found in any of the viscera, except the heart; and very often, the extent of the actual disease, bears no proportion to the urgency of the previous symptoms. I have met with cases where the disease had proceeded with amazing rapidity to a fatal issue, and yet where on dissection I found the heart only partially affected. The chronic inflammation, therefore, is a much more dangerous disease than dilatation of the heart; it runs its course more rapidly, and is not characterized by such well defined symptoms as those produced by simple dilatation. Although these two diseases be essentially different in their nature, and degree of fatality, yet they are not, in practical works, sufficiently accurately distinguished from each other. Dr. Ferrier seems to consider dilatation accompanied with chronic inflammation, as the same disease with simple dilatation. This is, however, what no one who has had an opportunity of tracing the progress, and watch-

ing the effects of these diseases can ever admit.
Nay, all the symptoms of chronic inflammation,
even to the pulsating tumor *in epigastrio*, are
present, when, on dissection, not a trace can be
seen of dilatation of either side of the heart.
We cannot therefore look on dilatation and
chronic inflammation, accompanied with dilatation, as the same disease; we often see them
separate, and frequently, observe the one terminate in the other. My brother, many years ago,
dissected a case of this kind. The patient, a poor
boy of the name of Stirling, had for some months,
been a patient in the hospital, for the cure of
dropsical complaints; he took different diuretics,
without much alteration for the better, and at
last, the pulse began to lessen in point of frequency; it descended even so low as to thirty
beats in the course of the minute, and was full
and sluggish. He remained in this state for a
few weeks, when he was attacked with a febrile
affection; the pulse instantly became preternaturally frequent, ranging from 120 to 140
strokes in the minute; and the heart, which had
formerly been felt beating low in the thorax,
now rapidly appeared to descend into the epigastrium, where there was a fixed pain. The other
symptoms were precisely such as accompany
chronic inflammation of the heart, and the termination was speedily fatal, after the accession
of this change. This case illustrates clearly
the dissimilarity of these two diseases, and

shews that dilatation of itself is not so dangerous as when accompanied with chronic inflammation, which is one of the most deceitful diseases of the heart; often making its appearance
without any obvious cause, and carrying off the
patient before it is ascertained whether this organ
be really affected. From the history of this
complaint it will appear, that the chief morbid
symptoms are referred to some distant part, or,
if by chance, any pain be felt in the thorax, it
is dull and fugitive. Ruysch, in his *Thes:
Anatom.* mentions, that in one case, the heart
was found, after excruciating pain in the region
of that organ accompanied with an acute fever,
completely adhering to the pericardium. In
this patient, it would from other circumstances
appear, that the accretion of the pericardium
had been the result of carditis, a disease very
unlike chronic inflammation. So very deceitful
is this affection, that pus, or rather a lymphatic
secretion resembling it, is frequently formed
without any suspicion of the presence of local
inflammation. I very much suspect, that the
patient whose case is hinted at by Dr. Fordyce,
had died of this complaint. So vague and
irregular are its symptoms, and so Proteus-
like are its forms, that were a patient with this
affection presented to a practitioner, who had
not had several opportunities of seeing the progress of the disease, and of witnessing the dissection of such as had died from it, he would,

from the contemplation of the attendant symptoms, suspect any other organ sooner than the
heart, and the presence of any other morbid
condition rather than inflammation, or any of
its modifications. This disease, except in so far
as it produces adhesion of two contiguous surfaces, and often a secretion of a flaky fluid, presents not a single feature belonging to inflammation. A practitioner therefore, who had not
bestowed considerable attention in acquiring a
knowledge of clinical medicine, would, if called
to treat a case of this disease, feel himself completely bewildered; he would find a patient
with a set of anomalous symptoms, with a small,
frequent, and jarring pulse; a bloated anxious
countenance, a fixed pain in the pelvis, or at
the pit of the stomach, where, perhaps a firm
tumour would be felt beating with furious pulsation. The patient would say, that he had
never felt pain in the chest, that he had little
or no uneasiness about the heart; assertions,
which, unless the physician knew the ambiguous nature of the complaint he had to treat,
would lead him far from the real seat of the
disease. I could, to impress this more firmly
on your mind, relate several histories of cases
of this disease, either altogether misunderstood,
or very mnch mistreated. I do not, however,
know that this would be much for your advantage; I shall therefore merely state a few of the
leading circumstances, in one or two cases, and

point out the source of doubt. One case, that of a strong athletic man, made a particular impression on me. He was a publican, who was given to drinking, but after free indulgence, he was seized with shivering, a small, hard, and frequent pulse, attended with great anxiety of countenance, a constant pain in the pelvis, and complete retention of urine. He was bled, put into the warm bath, and blistered over the pubis, but all would not do. The catheter was introduced, and some urine drawn off; this, however, was productive of no alleviation of the symptoms; no more was purging. The man sunk into a comatose state, muttering incoherently. This change in the complexion of his disease, was considered as indicative of the necessity of shaving the head and blistering it; both were accordingly done, but the man died.

THE case was curious, from the appearances presented by dissection. The brain was healthy, hardly a drop of water being lodged in its cavities, no fluid was effused between its membranes, nor were its vessels very turgid with blood ; in the abdomen every viscus was to appearance as healthy as the brain, and the bladder of urine, which before death, seemed to be the chief seat of disease, was slightly distended, and not at all painted with vessels. The pericardium was firmly attached to the heart, insomuch, that it required some dissection to ascertain whether or not that capsule was wanting.

It formed by the closeness of its union, a part of the heart, except at a few spots where a small quantity of flaky lymph was interposed between them.

THE examination of this body led to the discovery of some curious phenomena, and to results, which *a priroi* could not have been expected. All the viscera and organs were sound, except the heart, which few, from the previous symptoms, would have expected to have found deranged. If any conjecture had been formed before death, it would have been that the urinary bladder was diseased; a supposition which might have been rendered probable by taking into account the accession of coma, subsequent to retention of the urine. I hardly indeed know any symptom by which the real nature of the disease could in this instance have been detected, nor do I see that the practitioner was at all culpable for his plan of treatment.

I HAVE just related the history of a case, where chronic inflammation of the heart put on the resemblance of a disease in the bladder; I may notice another instance, where it assumed the likeness of a uterine affection. A stout, healthy, well made, middle aged lady, of a cheerful disposition, and who had been in a hot climate, complained on the 27th of February, 1807, of a tickling cough, languor, and a fixed pain in the region of the right kidney. Her ailment, as she was advanced in pregnancy of her third child, did not excite much alarm. She took, however, a mixture composed of ammoniated tincture of opium, conjoined with squill vinegar, by which the cough was completely removed, and the pain in the kidney soon gave way to the action of a synapism. She had no return of her complaint till the 23d of March, when she was seized with severe pain in the bowels, accompanied with tenesmus, and a sensation as if the uterus had subsided into the pelvis. The bowel complaint was entirely removed by two doses of castor oil, followed up by the use of anodyne clysters. On the 2d of April, the bowel complaint returned, accompanied with copious bilious vomiting, and on the morning of the 3d, labour pains came on, and in a few hours, she was delivered of a dead child about the eighth month. After the delivery of the fœtus, the vomiting became more constant and distressing, notwithstanding the liberal use of anodynes. On the morning of the 4th, she for the first time complained of wandering pains about the right side of the chest, and the vomiting had become almost incessant. Through the day, she took a draught, containing a considerable quantity of ammoniated tincture of opium, which completely checked the vomiting, but the cough and flitting pains in the heart continued, and the lochial discharge was very sparing. Next day she was much in the same state, only her countenance was more anxious,

and the pulse was very small and frequent. She
was desired to rub the side of the chest with
camphorated oil of turpentine, and as on the
7th, the vomiting had recurred, a large blister
was applied over the pit of the stomach. By
these, the pain in the chest and the vomiting
were entirely removed, and neither of them ever
returned; but on the 8th, she complained of
headach, and most excruciating pain in the pelvis, and the lochial discharge was altogether
suppressed; she moaned and became delirious,
and although on the first appearance of the
uterine affection, twelve ounces of blood had
been taken from her arm, still the pain was in
no degree abated, but rather increased till about
three o'clock, when she expired.

THE day after her death, the body was opened, when, contrary to expectation, the uterus
was found quite healthy, and not a single vestige of disease of any kind was to be seen about
the abdominal viscera, but the right lung which
was tuberculated, adhered to the mediastinum
and pericardium, and the latter was in some
spots glued to the right side of the heart. On
both the outer and inner surface of the pericardium, a quantity of oily lymphatic flaky fluid,
resembling pus, was deposited, and wherever
the pleura or heart were in contact with this
matter, they seemed as if boiled in pus.

THE review of this case, will furnish an in-
structive lesson; a patient lost, not from negli-

gence or want of zeal on the part of the practitioner, nor yet from culpable ignorance of his
profession, for here the cause of disease was in-
volved in obscurity. It will lay before you a
fact which no practitioner ought ever for a moment to lose sight of, and will impress on your
minds, the absolute necessity of persevering industry in the pursuit of professional knowledge;
and will convince you, how much those engag-
ed in the highly responsible duties of actual
practice, have occasion to lament the imperfection of diagnosis. In this patient, there were no
signs by which one could have been led to suspect the existence of disease in the heart; the
pain in the thorax was not present at the commencement of the complaint, and it altogether
disappeared some time before the fatal termination. Guided by the frequency of the pulse,
the irritability of the stomach, and the paucity
of the lochial discharge, one could hardly have
doubted, but that most, if not all the symptoms
were dependent on abdominal irritation. If
any doubt arose, it was from the absence of
tension of the belly, which is an almost invariable concomitant of such a state of the uterine
system as was suspected, a condition which the
accoucheur dreads, because few recover from it.
When the uterus became so morbidly and ex-
quisitely sensible, no one could have hesitated
respecting the existence of disease in the pelvis; the *tout ensemble* of the symptoms, admo-

nished the practitioner of the presence of a
highly morbid condition of the womb. From
the beginning to the end of the complaint, there
did not exist a single symptom, which could have
given rise to a supposition of the real nature of
the complaint. No one ever suspected, that either the pericardium or heart was diseased,
but all who saw the patient, knew from the
clouded anxious countenance, and the frequent
small pulse, that something material was wrong;
but the fatal issue came very unexpectedly, and
it was left for dissection, to elucidate the cause
of disease, and to prove the fallacy of all the conjectures respecting the nature of the complaint.
On examination, the practitioner found all the
viscera which were suspected to be deranged, as
healthy as it is possible to conceive them to be,
and saw that the very organ, which was never
viewed as having any connection with the complaint, was in reality the cause of all the symptoms. In mistaking the nature and seat of the
disease, the practitioner was surely not to blame,
for in this instance, from the adhesion of the
pericardium to the heart being partial, there
was no conspicuous jarring in the thorax, nor
pulsation in the epigastric region; there was no
apparent enlargement of the heart. The absence of these, rendered the affection of this
organ very obscure. Besides, if we recollect,
that after delivery, the lochial secretion was
obstructed, along with other signs indicative

of an uterine disease, we shall not wonder why the attention was chiefly turned to the abdominal viscera. It is always more or less difficult to distinguish this condition of the thoracic viscera; but in the puerperal state, the obscurity is increased tenfold; and he who can overlook the apparent symptoms, and turn his attention to the distant disease, must have seen and lost a number of cases.

I HAVE just stated, that chronic inflammation of the heart, may assume the symptoms of an affection of some distant part, without at the same time any actual disease existing in the parts. I must next observe, that this disease is sometimes really conjoined with other morbid affections, especially of the lungs. I have by me a preparation procured from a young woman, who was reputed to have died of phthisis pulmonalis, but who in reality died from a mixed disease. On opening the body, the left lung was a mere bag full of pus, a vomica of immense magnitude, all the substance of the lung was removed by absorption, except a thin strip at the root, the pleuretic covering alone remained at the boundary of the abscess. The pleura was much thickened, and adhered firmly to the whole extent of the pleura costalis, and also to the outer surface of the pericardium over the left ventricle of the heart. The capsule of the heart was much altered in its appearance, it was very thick, and over the whole surface of the left side of this organ, it adhered with much firmness. The bond of union was by shreds of a lymphatic looking substance. Over the right side a profusion of a similar lymphatic matter was spread, and the same was likewise found lining the inner surface of the corresponding portion of the pericardium, and in little sacs between them, an oily puriform looking fluid was collected. It was not pus, nor in this disease, is it ever pus, it is only a secretion bearing a nearer resemblance to purulent matter, than to any thing else with which I can compare it. The pulmonary abscess really contained pus, and the heart and the pericardium had the look of having been boiled in purulent matter, although the pericardium did not contain a single drop of real pus,

THE case of this patient was very ill defined, chiefly owing to Mr. De Lys, at that time house-surgeon in the hospital, not being able to procure satisfactory answers to his questions; he learned however, " that she was affected with " frequent, but not severe cough, attended with " dyspnœa and ineffectual efforts to expecto- " rate. She complained of constant pain in the " epigastric region, and in the left side of the " thorax, and lay most at ease on her back. " The pulse was about 112, and hardly percep- " tible." In a case related by Keyer, " the pulse " was small and weak as in this patient, the " countenance was languid, she was much ema-

" ciated, extremely debilitated, and had fre-
" quent threatenings of syncope. She passed
" restless nights, her appetite was impair-
" ed, she had great thirst, her bowels were
" loose, but menstruation was regular." These
I consider as the symptoms more immediately
belonging to the affection of the heart and lungs,
and from reviewing them, you will at once perceive, that the symptoms are not precisely such
as would individually belong to the disease in either of these parts. By the blending of these two
affections, the morbid phenomena are considerably modified. She had likewise paralysis of the
upper part of her body, she complained of vertigo and tinnitus aurium, which I refer to the affection of the head, although Dr. Ferrier mentions,
that some of his patients, who had chronic inflammation of the heart, compared the ringing
in their ears to the beating of hammers. " She
" was unable to walk, and had in a great mea-
" sure lost the power of swallowing, and the
" faculty of articulation. The tongue was flac-
" cid, and its muscles paralytic." This was
the account Mr. De Lys procured of the woman, who was about thirty years of age, when
admitted as a patient into the hospital, on the
27th of September, 1806.

" HER complaint had then continued for a
" twelve month, and the paralytic symptoms
" were the first she perceived. She had applied
" several blisters to her head, and used other

" remedies with the nature of which she was
" unacquainted, but believed herself the better
" for them."

TOWARD the latter part of her life she complained more of the pain in her breast, also of the dyspnœa, and the tendency to syncope became more distressing. During her treatment in the hospital, she was blistered over the sternum, and was directed to make use of a cordial mixture and wine. Without any precursory aggravation of the symptoms, she suddenly expired in the month of October, 1806.

ON this case, I may remark, that urgent as the symptoms were, they did not by any means bear a proportion to the complication of disease and the extent of organic affection. To prove this, need I do more than merely say, that although the pericardium embraced the whole extent of the heart by morbid union, she never complained of the distressing pulsation in epigastrio, nor of the jarring in the chest; she did indeed complain of pain about the epigastrium, but she never made mention of any heaving or tumour there. Extensive as the ravages of the disease were, no pathognomonic symptom was predominant; the physician was compelled to guess at the nature and seat of the complaint. Considering the stage of the disease at which the patient came under his care, and the prostration of strength which he witnessed, he was certainly excusable in administering cordials and wine in the decline of this person's life; but still these unquestionably would accelerate the fatal issue. For we uniformly find, that in almost every organic lesion of the heart, stimuli are the bane of the patient. I believe that cordials prescribed with the view of supporting the fleeting strength, are often more destructive to the patient than even the disease. I have known more fatal examples of this kind than it would be prudent to mention.

LONG after these observations were written, I was favoured with a very interesting case by Dr. Brown. The disease was a very complicated one, for it was found on dissection that the pericardium adhered firmly to the heart, that this organ was dilated, and that the mitral valves were in a morbid condition. The patient was in the Edinburgh hospital under Dr. Rutherford's care, while Dr. Brown was house-surgeon. In Dr. Brown's notes of the case, I find it stated, " that the girl has pain under the point of the " sternum excited by a deep inspiration; the " pain, although not constant, prevents her from " lying on either side; when she turns to the " right side it is less increased than on the oppo- " site one; when she lies down, she has also " some cough, but the expectoration is easy. The " stroke of the heart is more than usually strong, " and it is felt both at the usual place, and at " the point of the sternum; she has palpita- " tion when in the horizontal posture, and the

" pulse is 112, of natural strength; she has much
" flatulence in the bowels, accompanied with
" pain in the stomach, which is alleviated by
" passing flatus; she has frequently shifting
" pains in several of the large joints; the
" ankles are in the evening slightly œdematous;
" the appetite, tongue, and bowels, are natural,
" and the skin is soft; the catameniæ are re-
" gular.

" WHEN the patient applied on the 2d of
" December for admission, she stated, that the
" stomach complaints had been of two weeks
" standing; that the cough had begun eight
" days before, and that the pain at the stomach,
" and palpitation had only made their appear-
" ance four days before. She had formerly been
" a patient of Dr. Duncan's, with rheumatisms,
" which had been cured.

" ON the 3d, she had a draught containing ʒj.
" of ether, and she was directed to bathe her
" feet.

" ON the 5th, in addition to her former com-
" plaints, she has now pain at the top of the
" sternum, at the point of the left shoulder, and
" along the outer part of the arm."

ON the 8th, Dr. Rutherford's report is, " Pains
" continue. The pulsation of the heart is un-
" usually strong, accompanied with a jarring
" motion, most remarkable at the contraction
" of the ventricles, and when she lies upon the
" right side, then it is perceptible, also at the

" contraction of the auricle ; pulse rather quick-
" er than usual, small and compressible. The
" sensation is particularly disagreeable when
" she first lies down on either side ; sleep pretty
" calm, but she awakes frequently, from the
" pain in the shoulder and arms stretching along
" the clavicle to the neck."

THE prescription for this day was to continue
the draught with Ether 3j. and Tinct. Opii. gtt.
xxxv. She was also directed to rub the arm
and pained parts with the Tinct. Saponis cum
Opio.

JANUARY 1st, " Little change on the pal-
" pitation, pulse quick, weak, but regular, cough
" frequent."

ON account of the teazing cough, she had a
mucilaginous mixture prescribed, containing
some Tinct. Opii.

TILL the 15th of the month she continued
nearly in the same state. On the evening of
that day, she had a fit of coughing, which excited considerable pain of the heart.

" ℞. Sol. Assæ Fœtid. ℥j.

" Tinct. Opii. gtt. x misce, capt. hora sexta.

BESIDES this medicine, she was directed to
continue the draught in the evening.

21st, More pain and palpitation ; she perceives the stroke more towards the spine than
formerly.

30th, Sense of oppression at the heart ; she
has often got dyspnœa independent of the cough.
Pulse quick, small and feeble.

SHE was this day directed to take a draught containing Tinct. Castor. Comp. ʒj. Aq. Menth. Pip. ʒss. three times a day, as occasion may require.

ON the 31st, there was this alteration, that occasionally her fingers are benumbed, when they are colder than natural, and livid.

FEBRUARY 3d, continues in the same state; " she has still the numbness, coldness, and livor " of the nails, especially towards evening, at " which time also her breathing is very much " affected."

FOR other five months her complaints became more and more distressing, and at last she died anasarcous.

AFTER death the body of this patient was very carefully examined. " The pericardium " was found firmly adhering to the heart; the " left auricle and ventricle were remarkably " large, particularly the auricle, which was " nearly the size of the fist; the opening be- " tween the auricle and ventricle was so large " as to admit four fingers. The mitral valve " was hardened, and so small in proportion to " the size of the aperture, that it could not pos- " sibly perform the office of a valve. The right " auricle and ventricle were both enlarged, al- " though not so much as the left."

I AM very glad to avail myself of Dr. Brown's permission to make use of this case, for I think it illustrates some of the facts which I have al-

ready detailed, and I am also more anxious to
bring it forward, as I find, that in it, the distant
pain was referred to a part which I have not
formerly known affected. I have indeed in one
or two cases of diseased heart, known the patients complain of pain about the shoulder, but
none of these were cases of chronic inflammation and adhesion of the pericardium; and in
simple dilatation of the heart, Bartholine saw
a patient suddenly expire, " Qui longo autem
" tempore abdominis dolores ad jugulum as-
" cendentes patiebatur ut inde se crederet suffo-
" cari." In this person, however, there was an
obvious reason for the pain, " conspiciebantur
" pulmones lividi et prope gulam inflammati."
But in the person whose history I had from Dr.
Brown, there was no inflammatory affection of
the pained parts; there was no obvious change
from their healthy condition. You have also
observed, that the pain was not confined to the
shoulder and arm, but that it was felt at the
point of the sternum, and also toward the close
of the patient's life in the chest. The case is
also highly interesting, from the very accurate
reports taken by Dr. Rutherford, and also from
the ingenious explanation which he offers of
some of the symptoms. From the size of the
heart I am convinced, that it was not this organ
which was felt beating beneath the point of the
sternum; it was, on the contrary, I believe, the
repercussions of the liver, which produced the

pulsation there. I think there is also reason to suspect, that there was not real palpitation present. We can most clearly perceive from the detail of the case, that it must have been some other irregularity of action than that which constitutes palpitation. Dr. Rutherford does not say that he ever felt the palpitation; in all probability, therefore, had this attentive practitioner ever seen the patient while affected with the palpitation, he would have stated it in his report. His own testimony is decided in regard to what he felt when he examined the patient. His own words are, " The pulsation of " the heart is unusually strong, accompanied " with a jarring motion, most remarkable at the " contraction of the ventricles." This is what Dr. Rutherford says he perceived. The patient herself must have been sensible that the heart did not act in its usual way, and in all probability she vaguely called the sensation she experienced palpitation. Had Dr. R. mentioned that he felt the palpitation, I would never have ventured to dispute the authority of one so able to judge. When, however, I consider how liable a patient is to deception, in expressing sensations, and when I observe what has taken place with several of our own patients, I venture to express a doubt as to the reality of the presence of palpitation in this, or indeed in any case of extensive adhesion of the pericardium to the heart.

I FEEL more authorised to make these observations, from attending to what the celebrated Morgagni has written in his 23d epistle, on the seat and causes of diseases. In this letter, you will find a numerous collection of cases of adhesion of the pericardium to the heart, and on reviewing the histories, it is apparent, that palpitation is by no means reported to be a frequent symptom. This author states, that he has collected forty-five examples of the disease, and adds, " if you first set aside these six, which " do not tell us what disorders had preceded; " and in the next place, take away four-and- " twenty more in which no mention is made of " a palpitation, no more than fifteen will then " remain, wherein mention thereof is made ; " that is to say, two of Bellonius, and Hier- " nius, Stegmannus, the Genoese physicians, " Dionis, the English, Vieussens, Freind, Agri- " cola, Utrechtus, Haller, Le Fays, Pasta, and " Du Quaye, each of whom relate an observa- " tion." Morgagni after having ascertained that in these fifteen, palpitation had been reported to have been present, next endeavours to prove, that in these cases, the palpitation was not in reality dependent on the accretion of the pericardium to the heart, but was occasioned by some other cause. You thus perceive, that the different cases on record, tend to prove, that in general, no palpitation is present ; but it cannot be denied, that in a few of

the histories related before the time of Morgagni, and in many since his death, express
mention is made of the existence of this symptom. From what I myself have seen, however,
I would be inclined to believe, that some anomalous affection had been mistaken for palpitation, and not, as Morgagni supposes, that
this symptom had really been present, but produced by some other cause.

IT would be injustice to Dr. Rutherford,
not to mention his explanation of the cause
of jarring in the action of the heart. " The
" adhesion of the pericardium to the heart,
" impedes its free action, in consequence of the
" density, elasticity and tension of that mem-
" brane." He adds, " when the heart contracts,
" some force is required to corrugate that elas-
" tic dense membrane." In the history of the
symptoms, we find it mentioned, that on the
21st of January, she felt the " stroke of the
" heart more towards the spine than formerly."
Perhaps this may be explained by the exten-
sion of the attachment of the pericardium to
the auricles, producing a similar digging about
the base, as had formerly taken place at the
apex of the heart.

ON the treatment of this patient, I would observe, that it corroborates the observation I
made on the last case, previous to the time that
Dr. Brown communicated this history to me. It
shews that opium and stimuli only exasperate

the symptoms. You will observe, that in the prescription for the 15th, she was ordered to take a fœtid draught every three hours. She did so, and at the very next report, it is mentioned, " more pain and palpitation." She persisted still in the use of her medicines, and in the report of the 30th, it is stated, " sense of op-
" pression at the breast; she has often dyspnœa
" independent of the cough; pulse quick, small,
" and feeble." In short, the same medicines were continued, but without producing any good effect.

I HAVE just related a number of cases from the works of practical authors, and from my own observation, to shew, that in chronic inflammation of the heart, there is seldom any pain felt in the chest. A case of this affection in some respects curious, lately came under the notice of Dr. Poole, and was, after death, examined by that accurate anatomist Dr. Barclay, who politely sent me a description of the symptoms and morbid phenomena, with permission to publish them. Dr. Poole observes, " the pa-
" tient was aged fifty, a strong muscular man,
" rather above the usual height, no way corpu-
" lent, and of very temperate habits, by trade
" a mason." He had constant pain or rather soreness in the left side and breast; his breathing was generally laborious, and when going up a hill or stair, or when walking quick, was almost suspended. He was continually haras-

sed with a hard cough, and Dr. Poole says, " I
" was much struck, and on his account, greatly
" alarmed at the irregularity of his pulse, to
" which he claimed my particular attention, as
" he had long thought it a very *queer one* : at
" times, it did not make above thirty beats in a
" minute, in consequence of an intermission fre-
" quently taking place, and continuing during
" a space in which from three to eight or more
" ordinary pulsations might have been perform-
" ed. This intermission, however, was so in-
" constant, and the irregularity of the beats so
" great, as to regard no ratio I could discover.
" The pulse was always exceedingly weak, small,
" and sunk, or so to speak, concealed. About
" two months before death, he became dropsi-
" cal in the lower extremities, and nearly about
" the same time, a swelling or protuberance
" was observable in the right hypocondrium,
" extending to the epigastrium; this was ex-
" ceeding painful on pressure, and continued till
" his death, without any perceptible change.
" The œdema of the limbs was removed, but
" his breathing became more and more difficult;
" and about a fortnight before his death, the
" whole of the right side became paralytic."

DR. BARCLAY opened the body, " and there
" were six English pints of water in the thorax.
" The lungs were tuberculous, and adhering to
" the pleura and pericardium; the left lung was
" much condensed, and incapable of expansion

" by air. The pericardium adhered to the
" parts with which it was in contact, through
" the medium of a layer of organised coagula-
" ble lymph of a very pale straw colour ; this
" by a slight force, was readily separated from
" both the heart and pericardium. The apex
" of the heart was uncommonly soft for a space
" equal to the size of a filbert. On opening
" the heart, an aperture was found, in diameter
" as large as that of a goose quill, in the vesti-
" gium foraminis ovalis, by which the two auri-
" cles communicated."

THE preceding case is so remarkable, on account of the presence of pain in the region of
the heart, and the state of the pulse, that I
gladly avail myself of Dr. Barclay's permission
to make use of it.

IN this patient, the symptoms were so anomalous, as to present very little of the usual
character of chronic inflammation of the heart.
Had the body not been opened after death, or
had the examination been made by a less celebrated anatomist, we would, from the contemplation of the symptoms, have been inclined to
suppose, that death had taken place from disease of the valves. The intermission, smallness,
and sunk state of the pulse, the pain in the
chest, and the interruption of breathing on
walking fast or climbing a hill, are the usual
symptoms which attend a diseased state of the
valves of the heart. They rarely are produced

by chronic inflammation of this organ; their presence therefore in this case, affords an excellent illustration of the difficulty the practitioner experiences in discriminating between different diseases of the heart. I mention this to shew, how very guarded he of consequence ought to be, in giving his opinion on the nature of these affections.

FROM the cases which have just been related, it will appear, that the disease which has been named, although very improperly chronic inflammation of the heart and pericardium, is one which is not attended with the usual symptoms of chronic inflammation in any part of the body. Chronic inflammation of the heart, in so far as regards duration, is generally a very acute affection. In above twelve cases which have come under our review, it has begun and finished its career in the space of a few weeks, sometimes even of a few days. Were we to attend to the rapidity of its course alone, we would consider it as belonging to the active inflammatory affections, but it is in its complexion, altogether unlike carditis. From all, then, which has been said, we are led to conclude, that dilatation of the heart, chronic inflammation, and carditis, are essentially distinct in their nature and symptoms from each other. But it must be admitted, that simple dilatation very rarely runs its course without the accession of chronic inflammation, which I consider to be the reason why Dr. Ferrier, in his very valuable little tract on dilatation, has intermixed the histories of the two diseases, seeming to look on them merely as different stages of the same complaint. This author has also noticed, that the chronic inflammation is accompanied with a much more apparent than real enlargement of the heart; but he does not attempt an explanation of the cause of this deception; neither does he state, that when the pericardium is glued to the surface of the heart, the latter often appears both to the patient and the practitioner to be considerably dilated, while dissection shews that its capacity is in no degree changed. Previous to the fixture of the pericardium to the heart, I know of no symptom by which we can detect the presence of this morbid state of the thoracic viscera; but even after the union is completed, although the symptoms of disease be referred to a distant part, and although the patient be not sensible of any jarring in the chest, the practitioner may, by laying his hand over the heart, ascertain that it is neither acting in its wonted easy manner, nor yet is it confined to its usual place. Sometimes, however, the fatal issue takes place before the pericardium is so extensively adherent to the heart, as to give rise to the apparent action in the epigastrium. Cases of which, I have seen, and one has been described. From the absence of pain in the heart, and other causes, the nature of the complaint is previous to the adhesion of the pericardium to the heart, very ambiguous; afterwards, it is more easily detected. Dr. Ferrier says, " may we not therefore keep " the probability of chronic inflammation in " view, when the signs of dilatation are preced- " ed by fever, or attended with febrile symp- " toms; when their progress is unusually rapid, " without any obvious cause; when the pulse is " often quick; when there is much pain in the " lower part of the abdomen, without any af- " fection of the excretions?" If the latter symptom could be relied on, it would materially facilitate the diagnosis; but we have in the history of two cases, seen that the excretions were very far from being unaffected. In one person, there was an actual retention of the urine, and in another, a suppression of the lochial secretion. On this, therefore, we can place no dependence, neither can we rely on any sign, except the presence of a febrile affection, accompanied with the state of the pulse, which has already been pointed out, and the jarring pulsation in the chest, and undulation in epigastrio; where also no change takes place in the spot where the pulsation is felt in the chest, when the patient turns from side to side, we are assisted in our diagnosis. If these be present, we may certainly pronounce, that the patient has got what is called chronic inflammation of the heart and pericardium, a disease which would not appear alone confined to the thoracic viscera. Mr. Russel, some time ago, was called to visit a boy, who complained of agonizing pain in the shoulder, who was tormented with incessant vomiting, and who had also some pain in the belly. This patient notwithstanding the very judicious employment of such remedies, as are made use of in enteritis, died. On inspecting the body, it was found, that although the pain was concentrated about the shoulders, that, yet the actual disease was seated in the abdomen ; all the intestines were glued together, and between the bowels and peritoneum, there was lodged a quantity of light straw coloured oily looking fluid, which by an inattentive observer, might have been mistaken for pus ; the abdominal viscera presented nearly the same appearance that the heart and pericardium do, when affected with chronic inflammation ; from which, and the presence of the most acute pain in the shoulder, it is probable that the disease had been of the same kind. Among all the cases which we have met with, of this morbid affection of the heart, I do not recollect one, in which, if the disease had proceeded any length, there was not some straw coloured, puriform-looking, but lymphatic fluid, found in sacs ; and it is worthy of notice, that wherever this matter was effused, that there both the heart and pericardium, had the appearance as if their outer cellular coverings had been unraveled, and allowed to hang in shreds into the more fluid lymph.

I HAVE thus, in as far as our opportunities will permit, described the nature and consequences of a diseased condition of the heart, and its coverings, very frequently met with, and as yet very much misunderstood, although it has been known since the time of Bellonius, who toward the end of the 16th century, noticed the pericardium adhering to the heart in two dropsical subjects. From the application of the epithet *chronic* to this affection, one would be led to a belief, that the disease was tedious in its progress; in reality, however, it is the very reverse; it can, therefore, only be considered as chronic, in so far as it does not produce any conspicuous pain in the part affected. If we know little of the nature of this disease, we know still less respecting the proper mode of cure. Detraction of blood has been employed, but never with the marked advantage which results from its use in simple inflammation; and in those cases in which we have seen the lancet used in the advanced stage of the complaint, it has generally been productive of positive evil, rendering the breathing more oppressed, and the distant pain more pungent, at least this has happened in two instances which have come to my knowledge. As there is generally flatulence about the stomach, and torpidity of the bowels, I have seen laxatives conjoined with aromatics of marked advantage; but of all the remedies which we can employ, repeated blis-

ters over the sternum claim the preference ; or
equal benefit may be derived from the introduction of a seton or pea-issue over the situation
of the heart. By the use of laxatives, carminatives, and blisters, we can in the very advanced stage of the complaint, have it sometimes
in our power, to alleviate the most distressing
symptoms ; such as the terrifying dreams, incu-
bus and syncope, and where there are dropsical
effusions present, which is generally the case,
more especially, as Dr. Ferrier remarks, producing œdema of the face, the employment of
diuretics can on no account be dispensed with.
If we add the use of digitalis or squills to the
other remedies, it is often astonishing to see
the rapid amendment which for a time takes
place. Sometimes by their use, the patient who
could only breathe easily when leaning forward on a chair or table, has been so much relieved, as to be able to breathe pretty freely
even in the recumbent posture. But it is proper
to recollect, that as yet all the remedies prescribed, have only palliated, they have never in
any well marked case, cured the complaint. We
have therefore after all that has been said,
much reason to confess our ignorance both of
the nature, causes, and proper mode of cure
of this most dangerous disease.

HAVING endeavoured, in so far as our own
cases enable me, to describe the symptoms and
morbid appearances discovered on the dissec-

tion of those who have died from chronic inflammation, and adhesion of the pericardium to the heart; I may next notice, that this disease was not unknown to our predecessors, but being often accompanied with dilatation of the heart, it has generally been considered merely as a stage of that complaint; even where it was evidenly met with by itself, it was hardly considered as a distinct or peculiar disease. It has by various authors been described as " pe-" ricardium cordi accretum." I shall not recur to the very ancient writers for proofs that they had seen cases of this disease, but I may select a few of the best marked cases of this morbid affection to be met with in books. Lieutaud in his *Historia Anatomica Medica*, has collected a number of cases of this disease, but without being the least aware of the peculiarity of the affection; indeed most of the histories in his work are very imperfectly related, and are above all deficient in what regards the symptoms. OBSERVAT. 405, contains the history of a case by Portal, very nearly allied to the case of the lady I formerly described. In the female attended by Portal, the abdominal complaint was most prominent; she was advanced in pregnancy; and as in our case, had been delivered of a dead fœtus; the lochiæ were suppressed, she was drenched in cold sweats, and wrung with convulsions, till she died.

IN our case, the uterus was of the size that it

ought to have been, considering the time the
patient lived after delivery, and the stage of gestation at which she was delivered; but in Portal's case, the uterus and its appendages were
very large; the uterus occupied almost all the
abdomen, forcing the intestines backward and
upward, and its cavity was crammed with clot-
ted blood. In every other respect, the viscera
of the abdomen were healthy. With regard to
the heart and pericardium, he observes, " cordis
" pericardio accreti stupenda erat moles," in
both ventricles lymphatic concretions were contained.

A case by Fanton, forms OBSERVAT. 406.
It is a well marked instance of adhesion of the
pericardium to the heart. The patient, a man,
complained of great anxiety in the chest, but
the fixed pain was about the ensiform cartilage.
The violence of the palpitation was such that
it was both audible and visible at a distance;
the breathing was difficult, so that he was obliged to sit erect. Four or five times in the space
of two years he was nearly suffocated, " veribus
" postremo deficientibus obiit."

" Pulmones erant semiconsumpti; cor mole
" maximum, et vere monstrosum sese obtulit,
" pluribus exiguis ulceribus in superficie exe-
" sum et pericardio accretum."

IN this person the new and irregular action
of the heart was mistaken for real palpitation,
which, as we shall afterward see, could not be

present where the adhesion was so extensive, and the heart so large. It is to be regretted that the state of the pulse in the commencement and decline of the complaint, has passed unnoticed. Had this been attended to, in all probability it would have been found, that this man had first had a slow, and then a frequent pulse; for his case in many respects, is like to that of the boy Stirling, dissected by my brother. It also in the condition in which the lungs were found, resembles the case of the female who died in the hospital. The dissection elucidated very clearly the nature of the complaint; but if ulceration really was present, it would be a curious fact, and one which we have never seen to have taken place in any instance of this disease which we have dissected. I rather suspect that the narrator of the morbid appearances had mistaken the peculiar effusion, which is found in this disease for pus; and if so, it would have been contrary to the doctrines of the day, to have supposed that purulent matter could be formed without breach of substance.

OBSERVAT. 419, is a very incomplete history, but yet it is sufficient to illustrate the fact, that in chronic inflammation, the pain is not seated exactly in the part affected. The patient had difficulty of breathing, " cum quodam do- " lore circa mucronatem cartilaginem." This is all that is said respecting the symptoms, and no wonder, for the patient died while his physicians were disputing about the nature of his disease.

" Corpore examini anatomico subjecto, cor " tantæ magnitudines apparuit, ut triplo major " cavitatem totam fere occuparet et pericardio " ubique adhæreret. Pulmones vero exiles, sed " nulla læsione tacti deprehendebantur."

UNDER the title " Cor Crusta Obductum," Lieutaud has described two very excellent cases of chronic inflammation, and adhesion of the pericardium. The first observation 469, is more fully narrated, than his cases usually are, yet he has not mentioned the state of the pulse.

" VIRGO viginti annorum, ultimis vitæ tem- " poribus, suppressione mensium laborabat. Ac- " cesserunt difficilis respiratio, tussicula, febri- " cula, dolores pungitivi circa scapulas, anxie- " tates, appetitus prostratus, et tumor pedum ; " donec tandem repentina ventriculi inflamma- " tio cum subsequente vomitu ratione, et subi- " tanea denique suffocatione, miseriæ finem im- " posuisset."

THE right side of the chest contained water, and the lung on that side was loaded with very hard tubercles ; the heart was covered with a fat flaky matter, and adhering to the pericardium.

YOU would notice, that it is stated in the history of the case, that on the accession of inflammation of the stomach, and vomiting, the breathing became more difficult, and she died. Was

this state of the stomach only inferred from the
symptoms, or was it really discovered by dissection, that this viscus had been in a state of
inflammation? I think the former is the more
probable of the two, for in the detail of morbid
appearances, not a word is said about the stomach. Had this viscus really been found in a
state of disease, it would hardly have been overlooked; but in truth, we often find vomiting, and
very obstinate vomiting, attendant on this state
of the heart; and that, where by dissection, we
cannot trace a single vestige of actual disease in
the stomach, although, from contemplating the
symptoms, we might have expected to meet with
high marks of inflammatory action in this organ. The peculiarity of the fat flaky matter is
very decided in this case, as well as in the next,
where after difficulty of breathing, anxiety,
weight about the præcordia, and irregular fever,
the patient died; " et reperitur cor crusta qua-
" dam villosa obductum, qua passim pericardio
" annectebatur."

THE chapter entitled " Pericardium Cordi
" Accretum," contains several cases of chronic
inflammation of the heart. OBSERVAT. 695, is
a complicated case, ill narrated, and very incomplete. The lungs adhered every where to
the parts with which they were in contact; the
pericardium was inseparably joined to the auricles and large vessels. As the symptoms are
very imperfectly enumerated, we cannot from

them, judge whether the same effect had been produced by the attachment of the pericardium to the auricles, as results from its union with the ventricles. I would, however, rather be inclined to suppose, that although the one disease be equally fatal as the other, yet the former is seldom productive of the *pulsatio simulata* in the epigastric region. In some of our own cases, this has been decided. Even where the pericardium does adhere to the whole surface of the heart, if at the same time there be a complete matting of the neighbouring parts, the pulsating tumor in epigastrio is ill defined; there is, for a reason, which we shall afterward explain, more of a diffused undulation than of decided pulsation.

OBSERVATION 697, is the history of a boy about the age of puberty, and asthmatical, related by Peyer. This patient complained of *pain in the groin*; the pulse became small and tremulous, or jarring, " pulsus erat parvus et tre-
" mulus," he was tormented with anxiety, most difficult breathing, and slight cough; the belly, limbs, and genitals became œdematous, and swelled so as to threaten bursting.

" PULMO dexter pleuræ diaphragmati et pe-
" ricardio arcte hærebat, pericardium crassis-
" simum cordi undique erat adglutinatum."

IN this patient, the pain in the groins, the state of the pulse, and the supervention of dropsy, all proclaim the disease to have been similar

to the one described by Dr. Ferrier. The history is valuable, for in it the disease is more
clearly characterized than in most of the cases
related by Lieutaud. The particular mention
of the pain in the groins, renders it very interesting, as at that time no one could have a
preconceived idea, respecting the reference of
pain in this complaint to a distant part.

IN OBSERV. 699, by Lower, it is related that
the chief morbid sensation was referred to the
epigastrium, and that the person was subject to
syncope; and in the OBSERVATION following,
that difficult breathing, pain about the right sca-
pula, cough, weak intermittent pulse, pulsation
in epigastrio, and dropsical effusions carried off
the patient. The pericardium was firmly fixed
to the heart.

THESE are the best marked cases of this disease collected in Lieutaud's work. There are,
however, a great many others in which the
pericardium adhered to the heart; and yet,
where the distant pain was wanting; but, in few
or none, was there actual pain in the region of
the heart. As in most of the remaining cases,
either the state of the pulse has not been noticed, or the disease had been of years duration;
or, the previous state of the patient being unknown, we cannot therefore be certain of their
real nature. In one patient there was œdema of
the face, and in all of them, where any thing like
a history of the symptoms is given, there was dif-

ficulty in breathing, and cough, attended, as the
narrators of the cases describe, with palpitation
of the heart. In some instances, it is even
stated, that the palpitation was to such an extent, that the action of the heart was both visible and audible. This to me is incomprehensi-
ble; for I cannot conceive how palpitation of
the heart can take place, when the pericardium
is adhering to its surface. I can readily understand, how in this disease, the heart being
curbed in its motion, and having its action
considerably changed from the natural and
healthy one, may transmit new and morbid
impressions to the sensorium, feelings, which,
by the patient, are vaguely described as palpitation. If we go a step further, and enquire
what palpitation is, it will, I believe, be easy
to conceive, why this never does, or can take
place, except either in the incipient stage of the
disease, or when the adhesion is effected by long
filaments. When we are called to see a patient
with genuine nervous palpitation, we find the
heart, when we apply the hand over the chest,
acting more unrestrainedly than usual; it flutters in the thorax, and strikes confusedly against
the ribs. Still, however, this action is only a
modification of the healthy one, for we feel the
pulsations of the apex of the heart in the usual
place. There is just a sufficient deviation from
the healthy function, to make the mind take
cognizance of a variation. What are the phe-

nomena observable during the natural action of
the heart? If this had been strictly enquired
into, few would have related cases, where it is
said that, till the day of their death, the patients had palpitation of the heart; and where
after dissection, it has been stated, " *Cor vere*
" *passim pericardio hærebat.*" As the celebrated Senac has done.

WHILE investigating the action of the heart,
we are apt to overlook some circumstances; we
are apt to forget, that the auricles and ventricles
balance each other; and that while the one series
of cavities is contracting, the other is relaxing.
We are likewise liable to view the pericardium,
as of the same size with the heart, while in fact
it is only half the size; for it is demonstrable,
that in a state of health, more than one half of
the heart can never be in a state of distension
at the same time. The two auricles and ventricles act in succession; and in proportion to
the efflux of blood from the one, the blood flows
into the other. When the auricles are half contracted, the ventricles are half dilated, and *vice
versa.* This fact explains the phenomena seen
every day in the dissecting room, and shews
why, previous to injecting the heart, if the pericardium be slit open, this organ can be made
so much larger than when its capsule is left entire. If we, therefore, inject a healthy heart,
with the pericardium unopened, so far from ob-
taining a just notion respecting the size of its

cavities, we view them on a very reduced scale; for we have now divided between four cavities, the real measurements of two only. The heart injected with the pericardium entire, is taken in the aggregate of the size, which it has in the living body. But if we wish to see the real magnitude of its different cavities, we must open the pericardium, empty the cavities of the heart completely, pass a ligature round the foramen ventriculare on both sides, and then stitch up the pericardium. When we now inject the auricles, we see them in the real state they are in, when the ventricles are fully contracted in the living subject. I need hardly add, that, in making calculations of the quantity of blood sent out on each contraction of the auricle or ventricle, we must view them in this state.

DURING the action of the heart, the ventricular foramina and the apex, are the points most acted on. When the auricle is dilating, the foramen ventriculare is descending, and as the curved arteries are, as Dr. Hunter observes, at the same moment, by the influx of blood sent out by the ventricles, endeavouring, to bring themselves into a straight line, the opening between the auricle and ventricle, is thereby rendered more oblique than formerly. When now, the auricle is fully distended, it contracts, and propels its blood into the ventricle, by which, the foramen ventriculare is made to ascend, and the apex, which, during the action of

the ventricle, had moved forward so as to touch
the ribs, now returns to its proper station. As
soon as the ventricle is dilated, it begins to act
on its contents; its fibres shorten themselves,
the blood flows into the arteries, they tend to
a straight line; the distending auricles at the
same time push forward and downward the
posterior margin of the foramen ventriculare;
the apex of the heart by these two causes,
is carried forward till it comes in contact with
that part of the pericardium, which formerly invested the anterior convex surface of the right
ventricle; the flat surface of the heart moves
into the place of the apex, and the sinus venosus descends towards the diaphragm; the heart
thus rolls on its axis, and its apex impinges
against the left side of the chest. It is in this
way that the heart comes to be felt striking
against the ribs; and this can only take place,
when the heart and pericardium are permitted
to slide over each other. If we glue them
together, they move *en masse*; the apex of the
heart, can now no longer impinge against the
ribs, for it is incumbered by the pericardium,
which, instead of supporting it in its action like
a fascia, has now become a part of it. When the
ventricles contract, they drag the pericardium
along with them, and the pericardium again
pulls the diaphragm after it; so that thus by
the alternate elevation and depression of this

septum, the chief pulsation comes to be referred to the epigastrium, and a jarring only is felt in the place where the heart formerly beat. Thus, we are made acquainted with a fact, which may direct our diagnosis in practice. By tracing the changes, which in health produce the beating of the heart against the ribs, we have seen that palpitation, which is only a modification of the natural action, is incompatible with adhesion of the pericardium to the heart. By the regular change of position which takes place in health, all the parts of the heart act in unison. By the adhesion of the capsule to the heart, these changes are prevented, the heart and arteries assume an irregular and jarring mode of action, but palpitation can never make a part in the morbid phenomena.

PORTAL, in his *Cours d'Anatomie Medicale*, notices, among other morbid conditions, adhesion of the pericardium to the heart; he informs us of the various appearances which the bond of union assumes, and concludes, " Les adherences " du pericarde avec le cœur, ont eté reconnues " dans des personnes qui avoient eprouvé de la " difficulté de respirer; sur tout lorsqu'elles " etoient couchées des lipothymies frequentes, " et palpitations du cœur, telles que cet organe " paroissoit être dans un fremissement continuel, " le pouls etant irregulier et intermittent. Ces " malades avoient le visage, les mains, et les

" pieds œdemateux." From this account which
is very imperfect, we learn negatively indeed,
that there is not pain in the seat of the heart;
but the author does not notice that there is often an affection of the scrobiculus cordis, or
some distant part. The basis of his observations is contained in Lieutaud's work, but in
addition to the remarks of that author, he informs us that the face is generally œdematous.

BEFORE concluding the subject of adhesion
of the pericardium to the heart, I may mention,
that where this is induced by chronic inflammation, the bond of union is a flaky lymphatic
crust. We, however, in other cases find the one
fixed to the other by ligamentous-looking bands,
sometimes long, some times short, sometimes
the consequence of active inflammation, and
sometimes, to appearance, existing as an original
formation. Where the filaments are long, and
not the sequelæ of chronic inflammation, we cannot by any symptoms ascertain their presence,
any more than we can the thready adhesion of
the lungs to the pleura; but when the bands are
short, they are productive of imperfect action of
the heart. When these bands are the consequence of carditis, it would seem as if they
elongated themselves; at least it has happened,
in a person where the symptoms were for a
time troublesome, the disease gradually abated, and at the distance of many years, when

the body was dissected, bands were found of considerable length, stretched between the pericardium and the heart. I have myself seen one or two instances of bands passing from the pericardium to the heart; but as I know very little of the previous history of the subjects, I cannot be certain what symptoms were produced. Senac has detailed the history of two or three examples of this conformation. Two of these cases, form a part of the collection by Lieutaud.

OBSERVAT. 698, a. "Sexagenarius jampridem "asthmaticus, post pravam digestionem lypo- "thymia corripitur, pulsus scilicet obliteratur, "et omnia membra frigent. Dein respiratio fit "difficilior, et ipsi in solum dorsum decumbere "licet, alias imminet suffocatio. Post novem "dies inter hasce angustias è vivis derepente "decesset."

"SECTO cadavere, patet inter pericardium et "apicem cordis processus quidam ligamentosus, "brevissimus; cujus ope firmiter annecteban- "tur prædictæ partes."

OBSERVAT. 698. b. "Quidam pulsu debili et "quasi obliterato ad lypothymias summe pro- "clivis spirandi difficultate cum suffocationis "metu sæpius premebatur; post plures annos "inter hasce molestias fatis cessit."

"EXAMINI subjecto pectore occurrit in apice "cordis quidam processus ligamentosus duas li- "neas latus, et tres longus, subalbicans et den-

" sissimus, pericardio prope diaphragma im-
" plantatus."

As in both these cases, the bands were short
and attached to the apex of the heart, it is clear
that they must have curbed the healthy change
of position of the heart, and thus have rendered in some measure ineffective, the auricular
valves. These flaps can only perform their
function in perfection when they are pliant,
and when the foramen ventriculare is permitted
to descend to meet the apex, which rises upward and forward. By these bands the alteration in the position of the apex, would to a certain extent be prevented, therefore the valves
would only imperfectly cover the opening from
the auricle into the ventricle, and thus a part
of the blood, would, on the contraction of the
ventricle, be forced back into the auricle, and
also into the great veins about the neck and abdomen. From this view of the matter, it is demonstrable, that the symptoms must in some
measure resemble those produced by ossification
of the auricular valves.

It may be expected that I should at this time
compare the symptoms accompanying carditis,
or acute inflammation of the heart with those
attending the disease I have last described.
This on many accounts would be a very desirable object, but having never had an opportunity
of seeing a case of carditis, I scarcely feel my-

self qualified to lay before you a history of its symptoms.   I have in treating of many of the diseases of the heart, had occasion to differ from the statements given in books, of the symptoms of these affections.   I therefore think it better to be altogether silent on what I have not myself seen, than by copying merely from authors, to run the risk of misleading you.

OBSERVATIONS

ON THE EFFECTS PRODUCED BY DIMINUTION OF THE SIZE OF THE HEART.

WE sometimes meet with a condition of the heart precisely the reverse of dilatation.   We find occasionally all the cavities contracted, and in some instances the heart is so diminutive as to bear no proportion to the sanguiferous system.   In one case on opening an adult body, with the history of which I was unacquainted, I saw the heart little larger than it is often met with in a new born child.   In another instance I found the heart of a female twenty-six years of age, no larger than the same organ usually is in a girl of six.   In the preparation, the heart appears healthy in its structure.   The vessels are of a size proportioned to the age of the subject, but no more.   In opening bodies who have died in full vigour, we often find the heart apparently very much contracted, but this generally depends on the cavities containing little or no blood. Such examples have been brought forward as specimens of reduction of the size of the heart, but without the least shadow of propriety. We ought never to consider a heart as reduced in size, unless at the same time the pericardium be diminutive. Where we see the heart small, we should carefully examine the condition of the pericardium, for if it be found very disproportioned to the bulk of the organ it contains, we ought to decide without hesitation, that the heart was only reduced because its cavities were empty, and its fibres contracted. In cases of apparent diminution of the size of the heart, we ought also, as Portal very justly observes, to examine carefully the state of the neighbouring parts, when we shall most frequently find the reduction only symptomatic, produced by collections of fluid in the pericardium, or tumors pressing on it. Where the heart is too small for the system, the pulse will be frequent and small, the frame delicate If, however, the patient be predisposed to phthisis, then, as the vessels of the lungs are called on to act more frequently than they ought to do, we find that the irritation excites very serious disease, and in general the patient dies from ulcerated tubercles, or sometimes from pneumonia. This I saw happen in

a case which I had an opportunity of examining through the friendship of Mr. Short, surgeon
to the 26th regiment of foot.

To illustrate the effects of reduction of the
size of the heart, I may detail one or two
cases.

LIEUTAUD, *Obs.* 448, " Vir quinque et tri-
" ginta annos natus, gracilis et melancholicus
" de pectoris angustia conquerebatur cum tussi
" rara.   Accedunt febris lenta, cibi fastidium et
" macies ; sub hoc rerum statu ingruunt capitis
" et dorsi dolores cum vigiliis pertinacissimis.
" Dein ingravescit spirandi difficultas, febris ex-
" acerbatur, et erumpit alvi fluxus nulla arte
" domandus, atrophia demum confectus, inte-
" riit.

" RESERATO pectore deprehenduntur pulmo-
" nes lividi et schirrhosi.   Thymus simili ferme
" modo læsus conspicitur.   Cor vero aridum
" et mire contractum occurrit."

OBSERVAT. 453. " Quidam ab infantia de do-
" lore in pectoris latere sinistro querebatur,
" quo demum exacerbato occubuit."

" REPERIEBANTUR pulmones tumidi et macu-
" lis nigris notati.   Horum superficies innumeris
" vesiculis, atro humore turgidis obsita con-
" spiciebatur ; cor erat stupendæ exilitatis, adeo
" ut ad dimidium solitæ magnitudinis vix ac-
" cederet."

THE young woman whose heart hardly equalled the size of that of a child of six years of age,

had always been of a delicate make, but toler-ably healthy, till within fifteen months of her death; much about that time, she began to complain of pain in the chest, accompanied with difficulty in breathing, and cough. Mr. Russel now saw her, and on inquiry into the particulars of her situation he was informed, that she felt a considerable degree of pain in the abdomen; that she expectorated puriform matter, and suffered much from excessive debility. He was told likewise, that her nights were passed restless; that toward morning, she was drenched with perspiration; that her appetite was impaired, and her cough extremely trouble-some. The pulse was about 120 in the minute, small and feeble. Mr. Russel applied a blister to the thorax, desired her to take digitalis, which she did without benefit, and then he pre-scribed a few grains of oxyd of zinc, to be taken daily. By the blister, and while using the oxyd of zinc, her amendment was almost incredible, and a fair prospect was entertained of her com-plete recovery. When matters were in this pro-mising state, a relapse was occasioned by cir-cumstances which it is not necessary to men-tion; all her former symptoms recurred, but now the oxyd of zinc had lost its beneficial ef-fect; the stomach which had become extremely irritable, refused to retain it in any form. The pain in the abdomen was augmented, and an obscure tumor was perceived in the right hy-

pochondrium.   The pulse was always above 120,
but never exceeded 130.   Before her death, she
suffered severely from diarrhœa and nocturnal
perspiration, and for some weeks previous to
the fatal issue, her cough was incessant, and the
expectoration profuse.   In this state she linger-
ed for a length of time, her debility all the while
slowly increasing, and for some days before her
death, her limbs were so much distended with
water, that the skin threatened to burst.

ON the 26th of October 1806 she died, and
on the 28th, we obtained leave to examine the
body.   Both lungs were in a highly morbid
state, the left, however, was more diseased than
the right.   They were in texture in many parts
almost cartilaginous, and their substance was
excavated by abscesses.   In colour they were
dark, approaching to a gangrenous hue.   The
left side of the chest contained between two and
three pounds of fluid.   The pericardium was excessively small, and contained a still smaller
heart, and about an ounce and a half of serum.
All the abdominal viscera were healthy, except the spleen, which was very obviously enlarged, and also more pulpy than usual.   On
the left side, both the fallopian tube and ova-
rium were wanting, but the deficiency had existed as an original formation.

IN the first case which I have detailed of this
disease, you would observe, that Lieutaud
states, that the patient had cough, a slow fever

and wasting of the body; the only symptoms probably, which can justly be attributed to disease of the heart, and these you will see, are nearly the same as those described by Portal, as being produced by reduction of the size of this organ. " Cette diminution dans le vo- " lume naturel du cœur, a été reconnue dans " des sujets, qui etoient morts d'une fièvre lente, " avec une toux, une sensation de reserrment " de la portrine, &c." The difficulty of breathing in this person, was not I imagine, necessarily dependent on the state of the heart, but was produced by schirrhus of the lungs and thymus gland; a condition, which, independent of any disease of the heart, would in all probability have proved fatal. When to this we add the smallness of the heart, we shall not wonder that the man should have felt a tightness about the chest, and that " sub hoc verum statu ingruunt " capitis et dorsi dolores cum vigiliis pertina- " cissimis." In the second case, the symptoms of which, by the bye, are very vaguely reported, the lungs were found in a very diseased state; and in the third instance which came under our own notice, it would appear that the pulmonary disease had not begun till within one or two years of the patient's death: she had however always been delicate, and in her, there is every probability, that phthysis would have taken place, even though there had been no disease of the heart; for it is to be recollected, that diminution of the size of this organ, never can do more than merely act as an exciting cause of disease of the lungs in those predisposed. There is every reason to believe, that in this young woman, the predisposition was very great, for both her mother and others of the family, have since died of pulmonary consumption. Seeing that besides the natural tendency to disease in the lungs, there was also the irritation derived from the state of the circulation; you will doubtless feel surprised, that oxyd of zinc commonly considered a trifling medicine, or indeed any remedy, should so obviously palliate the symptoms. In her case, blisters and digitalis had both been tried without effect; when Mr. Russel thought, that perhaps, from the reputed qualities of oxyd of zinc, it might prove more beneficial. He tried it, and was pleased to find, that in this instance, he had not over-rated its powers. From the suspension of the disease, which evidently resulted from the use of this medicine in this case, we have been led to try its effects in other cases of pulmonary consumption. In some, it has for a season done good; but in others, it has altogether failed to alleviate, but in none has it exasperated the disease; which is saying more than we can do, with respect to some other remedies.

SINCE these remarks were written, my friend Dr. Gordon, Lecturer on Anatomy and Physiology in Edinburgh, has sent me a specimen of

a heart very much reduced in size. " It was
" procured from the body of an old woman,
" who seemed to have died of scrophulous en-
" largement of the mesenteric glands, and ex-
" tensive inflammation of the peritoneum." The
heart was exceedingly small, though not so small
as I have seen this organ in other instances,
and the left ventricle was thicker in proportion than the other parts. I mention it chiefly
on account of its presenting an appearance,
which I had never before seen so well marked.
There was a considerable serous effusion into
the aqueous membrane of this organ. The pericardiac covering was by this raised from the
muscular fibres, insomuch, that the surface of
the heart pitted on pressure.

As this state of the heart cannot be expected
to be removed, either by external or internal
remedies, and as we have seen, that the patients
are liable to disease in the lungs, our chief object must be to prevent the bad effects of pulmonary irritation. We must restrict the patient
to moderate diet, and enjoin a rigid abstinence
from spirits; and whenever we perceive the approach of pulmonary inflammation, we must
detract as much blood as the patient can bear;
we must apply repeated blisters over the chest,
and put the person on a very spare diet. Where
the complaint has proceeded the length of actual disease in the lungs, we must have recourse
to the same means we would employ in phthysis.

OBSERVATIONS

ON THE CONSEQUENCES RESULTING FROM CHANGE OF
STRUCTURE OF THE SUBSTANCE OF THE HEART.

MR. JOHN HUNTER very justly observes, that
a heart cannot be essentially necessary for circulating the blood, in as much as some animals
altogether want it. In the caterpillar tribe,
we have no defined heart; there is no reservoir
where the blood is collected to be delivered over
in quantity to the arteries. On the contrary,
the returning veins terminate directly in the artery which descends along the back of the animal; where it can, through the transparent
skin, be seen contracting on its contents, forcing them on with an undulatory motion. When
we ascend a step higher in the scale of being, we meet with an imperfect heart, and
in some tribes, we see this heart entirely appropriated to the pulmonic circulation, the
systemic being carried on as in the caterpillar,
by the arteries. In other varieties, the arrangement is recorded; we find no heart for propelling the blood into the pulmonary vessels,
but we perceive, that these vessels deliver over
their contents to a heart which is attached to
the systemic arteries. The fish has a pulmonic
heart; the snail a systemic one. These were

facts with which Mr. Hunter was familiar; I
cannot therefore conceive, what led this distinguished physiologist to conclude, that in the
human subject, the ventricle sends the blood
through the body, and is therefore the proper
heart, while the auricle is only an appendage.
Having once embraced this notion, he observes:
" And as the ventricle is the part, which pro-
" pels the blood to the different parts of the
" body, its muscular power must be adequate
" to that purpose, and therefore, it has a very
" strong muscular coat."

To prove that the auricles are subservient
to the ventricles, Mr. Hunter has stated, that
in those animals where the veins near the heart
are large, there is no auricle, and he has
convinced himself, and endeavoured to persuade others, that the ventricle is more valuable than the auricle; because, when the heart
is imperfect, we always find that the ventricle
is the part present. I should be very averse
to start objections to any of Mr. Hunter's opinions, for they are, in general, the result of
cautious induction from unquestionable facts.
Comprehensive and accurate as his views generally were, and elevated as his mind was above
the level of most of his predecessors, still it
would have been expecting too much to have
looked for absolute perfection in all his opinions;
although most of them have stood the test of
the strictest criticism, and are now considered as

axioms in medical science.   In appreciating
however, the relative value of the different parts
of the heart, and even of the heart itself, with
respect to other parts of the system, I think he
has erred.   For, although we regard in general,
the ventricles as stronger than the auricles, we
must not from thence conclude, that this is because the ventricles in a state of health are
" the chief agents in the circulation."   Until
we possess clear notions respecting the natural
function of a part, our ideas concerning its morbid actions, can never be otherwise than vague
and unsatisfactory.   But often our opinions regarding healthy function, are corrected, by observing what takes place in disease.   In the present instance, it is principally by attending to
the deviations from the natural condition, that
we come to a knowledge of the true relation
which the heart bears to the sanguiferous system.   It is only by the contemplation of such
hearts as that of Margaret Henderson, that we
are taught to reject the notions of the day, and
to view the heart, not as the most active agent
in the natural circulation, but merely as a reservoir to the arteries.   We may be still more
certain, that the heart does not circulate the
blood, from attending to what often takes place,
where the aortic valves are ossified.   It is a fact
well known, and fully substantiated by observation, that in this disease the heart contracts
sometimes twice for each pulsation of the arte-

ries, which could not happen, if in reality the heart by the *vis a tergo* drove on the blood. On the contrary, when so small a quantity of fluid is sent out from the ventricle, that the artery is not fully filled, it does not re-act on its contents, till the next contraction of the heart fills it ; then it acts, and then the pulse is again felt. If we would estimate justly the value of the heart, we must look on the auricles as reservoirs to the ventricles, and the latter again as serving the same purposes to their respective arteries.

THAT the ventricles during natural circulation, by their percussion, drive the blood along the vessels, is hard to conceive. To my apprehension, they only propel it with due vigour into the arteries, and they of themselves circulate it. The cases which are afterwards to be detailed, are clear and convincing proofs of this; and these afford an ample refutation of Mr. John Bell's conjecture, that the ductus arteriosus " gives the full force of the right ventricle to " the blood of the aorta, in addition to that of " the left ;" for in them the blood was circulated without the aid of either ventricle. Some have said, that the parts of the aorta near the heart, act vigorously on the blood, but that the parts more remote have need of the *vis a tergo* to drive on the fluid. If, however, it be admitted, and few will pretend to deny, that any portion of n artery, can propel its blood independent of any impulse communicated from the heart, surely we may be allowed to infer, that the whole artery can do as much; so that a vessel thirty-six feet in length, shall be just as capable of propelling its contents, as one of a single foot.

IT may naturally then be asked, why have we both an auricle and a ventricle, if the circulation can be carried on without either? In reply, I would observe, that according to the scheme of the perfect circulation, both parts are necessary. No doubt, we see in the lower ranks of the creation, that the animals do equally well without a heart as with one, or with a single, as a double heart. The caterpillar without a heart, discharges in perfection, all its necessary functions; and the fish, although it has no heart to propel the blood through its long and flexible body, yet circulates it with ease and regularity, by the sole unassisted action of its vessels. In none of these animals, however, do we find the functions so complicated as in man; their wants are few and simple; their mode of life and œconomy are fitted to their inferior rank in organization. Man, however, has other functions to perform, and other relations to maintain, and for the discharge of his multifarious duties, the structure of his frame requires to be more complicated; yet it is only so much so, as to fit him to hold the station which has been assigned him, in the scale of created beings.

IN the caterpillar, and its tribe, the body is small, and the vessels comparatively large; so that in them, there is no necessity for a reservoir to collect the blood, and to propel it into the artery in sufficient quantity to distend its canal. In the human subject however, from the proportion which the vessels bear to the body, a heart is rendered necessary; a reservoir is required to collect such a quantity of blood, as when impelled into the vessels, shall let them feel that they are in some degree distended. Besides, had there been only an aorta, and veins in the human subject, the blood could not of necessity, have circulated an equal number of times in a given period; neither could the pulsations have been equally frequent, if he had only had an auricle appended to his sanguiferous system. To circulate the blood sufficiently, frequently, and harmoniously, an auricle and ventricle are both provided. The auricle dilates, is filled, contracts, and propels its contents into the ventricle, and while the latter is acting on the fluid it contains, the auricle is again filling, and by the time that the ventricle is emptied, the auricle is ready to contract; thus the vascular system is always kept full, for the heart sends out just twice the quantity of blood, that it could have done with the same exertion, had there only been a ventricle. In this mechanism, I see a beautiful contrivance for furnishing such a quantity of arterial blood to the system, as

shall be sufficient for its wants; but I cannot
do otherwise than believe, that so long as the
heart and arteries continue healthy, they act in
a manner independent of each other; each performs its own part, but both tend to the same
purpose; unity results from their action.   Still
without being immediately fatal, one part of
the heart may lose its muscularity, or the arteries may have their power of contracting greatly impaired.   In the first instance, however,
that part of the heart which remains healthy,
performs besides its own functions, a considerable portion of the action belonging to the part
diseased; and in the latter case, the heart is compelled to act with redoubled vigour, for in proportion to the loss of arterial power, so is the
heart called on to make up the deficiency.   The
circulation can in either case be carried on, but
the vascular system is in a precarious state;
very trifling causes derange this mode of circulation; nay, in some cases put a final stop to it.

IN those cases where the arteries have lost
from ossification, their contracting power, the circulation is chiefly carried on by the percussive
action of the heart, aided indeed, by such parts
of the vascular system, as remain unaffected.
In all cases however, where the blood is circulated in this way, the pulse is feeble, and peculiar in the sensation; it communicates to the
finger, and the patients appear sallow and unhealthy.

HERE I would take occasion to mention, that many of the symptoms of an affection of the heart may be produced by this want of correspondence of the vascular system. I have known some cases, in which patients have died with well marked symptoms of diseased heart, where dissection clearly shewed, that this organ was healthy in its structure. The arteries were however found in so morbid a condition, as to prove that they had been incapable of due co-operation in carrying on the circulation.

IT is rare to meet with complete ossification of the vascular system, but different parts of the aorta are very liable to depositions of ossious matter between the coats. The disease is here however so partial, that it is productive of no great inconvenience. In a person whose body I dissected some time ago, I found the heart and aorta perfectly healthy, but the arteries of the head, pelvis, legs, and arms, were almost entirely ossified. In the arms, in the arterial trunks, the circles of bone are complete, and are not above the 100dth part of an inch distant from each other. In the lower extremities, the trunks are only partially affected, but the primary branches are nearly obliterated, they are not only ossified, but their inner surface is coated over with a lymphatic looking crust. They are so much ossified, that it is perfectly impossible that they could have assisted in circulating their contents, nay, from the incrustation in their canals, the blood would even find difficulty in moving along.

IN this person it is evident that the larger vessels must have had the burden of propelling the blood through the descending series. Application was made to those under whose care he had been, for information respecting his symptoms, and the cause of his death. Our inquiries have not been so satisfactory as we could have wished; all we have been able to learn is, that the man had been for some years in the East Indies, where he had like many others, drunk hard, had gonorrhœa, intermittent fever, and a liver complaint. Five years after his return from India, he had jaundice; and five weeks after that, he put himself under the care of a physician, who discovered that there was a degree of hardness in the right hypochondrium, but he could not ascertain that the liver was enlarged; the belly was however tense, and fluctuation was perceptible. The pulse was about 80, and the patient was weak and excessively languid. After he had been for a short time under the care of the physician, he felt himself gradually sinking, he fainted frequently without any very obvious cause, and the pulse was small and feeble. When matters were in this state, he was attacked with intermittent fever, and he then told, that he had also strictures in the urethra, which gave rise to considerable difficulty of passing his urine. Caustic was frequently applied to the strictures, the urine flowed easily, they were reported to be destroyed; but notwithstanding the use of the bark, cordials, and astringents, for he now had diarrhœa, he daily became weaker and weaker. He complained of pain about the shoulder and left arm, and the day before his death, an abscess was opened, in the vicinity of the shoulder joint.

THE information respecting the state of the circulation, is here so vague and unsatisfactory, that we can draw no inference from this case respecting the effects of ossification of the arteries; we know, however, from the testimony of others, that when the ossification of the arteries of a limb is complete, that then the action of the heart will not suffice, it cannot drive the blood all over the body, and therefore it happens, that gangrene of the extreme parts takes place. Mr. White of Manchester, when speaking about gangrene, observes, " there is one spe-" cies of mortification from an ossified artery, " which has ever been, and ever will remain the " *opprobrium medicorum.* The whole art of me-" decine is here in vain exhausted, and the " complaint continues uninterrupted in its fa-" tal progress, till it arrives at the extremity " of the ossification." If I am not misinformed, Dr. Monro has two specimens of ossified arteries, taken from limbs which were mortified.

YOU thus see, that though the heart be for a time capable of carrying on the circulation in some measure independent of the arteries, that yet the vascular system is but very imperfectly qualified to discharge its functions, and the persons are never healthy.   Let us next attend to the converse of this, and see how the arteries can discharge their offices, when a part of the heart is so much altered in its texture, as to have its contractile power destroyed.   Bordenave reports, that he met with a person whose heart was almost completely ossified.   We have also seen several cases in which the heart was much deranged in its structure, but still it has never fallen to our lot to meet with a single instance, in which both the auricles and ventricles were at the same time affected.   We have found the ventricles in one case mere calcareous moulds, and in another, we have seen both the ventricles cartilaginous; and in other instances, we have met with slighter deviations from the healthy structure of the ventricles.   But among all the examples of diseased hearts which have come under our notice, in one only has the auricle been in any degree deranged ; and in that case, it was of little consequence whether the auricle was healthy or the reverse, as the auricular valve was so malformed, that only a very small portion of blood could pass from the one cavity into the other.   That derangement of texture should more rarely affect the auricle than the ventricle, is a curious fact, and one which will require some explanation.   If the view which we have formerly presented of the action of the heart be a correct one, then we shall very readily understand how the ventricles may be ossified, and yet the circulation may be carried on. The ventricle may be ossified, and may be rigid as stone, and yet the blood may find its way into the arteries, and be fairly circulated through all the parts of the body. The circulation can be much better conducted without the action of the ventricles, than without the re-action of the arteries. For so long as the auricles remain healthy, they continue to receive, contain, and propel the blood into the ventricles; but if these be incapable of re-acting on their contents, the blood must stagnate in them till the next impulse from the auricle drives a part of it into the arteries, which urge it on by their single and unaided effort as in the fish. This I take to be the mode in which the circulation is conducted when the ventricles are ossified, or so much deranged in their structure, that they have lost their contractile power. In this plan of the circulation, the arteries never can receive their due quantity of blood, for no more can be sent into them than is displaced by the action of the auricles. There being, however, no valves between the auricles and veins, and there being an increased resistance on the part of the ventricle, a considerable portion of the contents of the auricle must be forced back into the veins, producing a pulsation in the neck, and undulation in epigastrio. The action of such a heart

is unharmonious and easily deranged, it can only act efficiently while the circulation remains
undisturbed.   If called on to increase its action,
it begins to jar, and is soon exhausted.   I have
already said, that when the ventricles have their
power annihilated, the auricles are necessitated, in part, to perform both their own functions and also that of the ventricles, and to accomplish this, it is required, that their muscularity be also augmented.   It is for this reason,
that we uniformly, when the ventricles are ossified, find the flesh of the auricles firmer and
stronger than usual.

I HAVE already more than once alluded to
the case of Margaret Henderson, a poor widow
woman, aged sixty, and the mother of several
children, who applied on the 26th of May,
1802, for admission into the Glasgow hospital.
She complained of cough, accompanied with
considerable expectoration of mucus, and attended with much difficulty in breathing.   The
inferior extremities were œdematous; the abdomen was enlarged; fluctuation was perceptible, with paucity of urine, but no thirst. A fixed
pain was seated in the right shoulder, and the
liver was evidently increased in size and indurated.   At this period, the pulse was small
but regular, and the appetite was unimpaired.
Diuretics, particularly the squill, removed the
symptoms completely, so that she was pronoun-
ced cured on the 23d of July, 1802.

THE same symptoms recurred on the 19th of October, but very speedily yielded to the same treatment.

SHE continued tolerably healthy till the 15th of January, 1803, when the former symptoms were renewed, but with this difference, that now the liver was more enlarged; no fluctuation could be distinguished in the abdomen; the legs pitted with extreme difficulty, and the attacks of dyspnœa were more frequent, and much more severe, occurring even occasionally through the day. The pulse was still regular, but of very unequal strength, and during the paroxysm of breathlessness, she more or less assumed a livid hue; at other times the surface was florid.

FOR two months previous to her death, which happened on the sixth of November, 1803, she was continually tormented with fits of nausea, complicated with great anxiety in the chest, and pain diffused over the abdomen. For a few days before her dissolution, the dyspnœa became constant, though still variable in point of severity, and ether ceased to have the power of alleviating to any considerable degree the symptoms. She was now compelled to continue constantly in a semi-erect position, a recumbent posture never failing to induce a paroxysm of breathlessness. The pulse which had hitherto been regular, now became feeble and intermittent; and in the notes of the case, with which Dr. Baird very obligingly furnished me, I find it expressly stated, that the patient never was affected with *palpitation or pain in the region of the heart*, nor uneasiness stretching into the arms; neither did she ever awake suddenly while dreaming, and in the latter part of her life, the urine in general measured six pounds *per diem*.

Two days before death, she had requested permission to visit her friends; she had scarcely however walked a few paces, when she complained of sinking, and it was with great difficulty that she accomplished her purpose. Next day, she was assisted back to the hospital, where she languished a few hours, and then expired.

On opening the thorax, the pericardium appeared at first sight healthy, but it was enormously loaded with fat. By more close inspection, however, independent of manual examination, we soon discovered an obvious deviation from the usual colour and structure of the part. Instead of the ligamentous, membranous appearance peculiar to the pericardium, it had assumed an opaque and dusky hue, a ragged spiculæ of bone likewise projected from its surface, rendering it very unequal. It adhered with the greatest tenacity to the parts in the vicinity, and where it invested the ventricles, it appeared incorporated with the substance of the heart. The whole extent of the pericardium covering the ventricles, and the ventricles themselves, except about a cubic inch at the apex of the heart, were ossified, and firm as the scull. Not

only the pericardium, but also the fleshy parietes of the ventricles, and some of the columnæ carneæ were changed into solid bone.
The ossified part formed a broad belt round the
ventricles of the heart.   Both auricles were
healthy, but thicker than usual, and no part of
the vascular system, which we examined, was
in the least degree morbid in its structure.

DR. BAIRD permitted me to take out the
heart, and it is now in the possession of Dr.
Monro.

IN this person, the pericardium adhered with
great firmness to almost the whole surface of
the heart; and I cannot but notice, that in the
history of the dissection recorded by Bordenave,
it is mentioned, that the capsule of the heart
adhered over the whole extent of that organ.
In this subject, the pericardium and substance
of the heart were very extensively ossified. But
it is worthy of observation, that this change of
structure, was confined to the ventricles; and I
may also remark, that the patient died after
having been for a length of time troubled with
dyspnœa, a sense of suffocation, and constant
anxiety about the chest.   In this subject, the
morbid appearances very nearly resembled those
seen on opening the body of Margaret Henderson; and you cannot have failed to notice,
that there was also a very great similarity in
the general symptoms of the patients.

THERE is another case of ossification of the

heart, related by Dr. Simmons, in which the pericardium which was very thin, and so firmly attached to the surface of the heart, that this capsule seemed to be wanting. The ossification
extended from the base to the apex of the heart,
in a line corresponding to the septum of this
organ, and here a portion of the auricle was affected. But from the change of structure being
very partial, and also from its position, it would
not materially impede the action of the auricles.
This I infer from the sinus venosus and auricle,
or portion of the auricle being unaffected. The
ossification would derange the function of the
ventricular valves, by preventing the apex from
approaching toward the base; but still I am inclined to think, that the adhesion of the pericardium would be more productive of deranged
action of the heart, than the ossification would.
We cannot, however, in this case, decide with
any certainty on the symptoms caused by this
affection of the heart, for along with the disease
of the heart, there was a morbid state of the
œsophagus. My chief inducement, therefore,
to refer to this history, is on account of the ossification being as in the two former cases, complicated with uniform adhesion of the pericardium to the heart. In some other instances which
have come to our knowledge, of partial ossification of this organ, the pericardium has been found
firmly fixed to its surface. From these facts,
it is very probable, that some who have been

supposed to have died from ossification of the heart, have really lost their lives from chronic inflammation and adhesion of the pericardium, the ossification being only a concomitant effect resulting from a common cause. In many cases, insulated pieces of bone, or tumors have been found in the heart, without any interruption of the function of that organ, and without any adhesion of the pericardium; but I have never known a case in which the ossification was extensive, where the capsule was not found adhering to the heart.

THE next case which I had occasion to see, was that of William Brown, a butcher, who had for many years had an affection of the heart, which twice, during intoxication, became so urgent, that he dropped down; the pulse ceased to beat, and he became livid and swollen in the face. By allowing him to lie at rest, he in both cases, slowly recovered.

IN the afternoon, just preceding his death, having been busily employed for an hour or two in some laborious occupation, he complained after it was done, of a greater than usual degree of oppression in the chest, accompanied with distressing headach. In consequence of his uneasiness, he went early to bed, where, about eleven o'clock he was found dead.

IN my notes of the dissection, I find it stated, " that the ventricles of the heart were found " completely changed in their structure, being

" now composed of a substance intermediate
" between fat and cartilage, and the auricles
" had their musculi pectinati much enlarged
" and redder than usual. The condition of the
" veins was not examined."

THE cases of Henderson and Brown, prove
most incontrovertibly, that the circulation may
be carried on without any assistance from the
ventricles; but they at the same time shew,
that in consequence of the deviation from the
natural function, the vascular actions are precarious and irregular. The auricles are of themselves competent to the performance of the
offices of the whole heart, but then they can
only accomplish this, while the circulation remains undisturbed. In the history of these
cases, you have noticed, that every increase in
the celerity of the circulation was followed by
an impaired state of the whole system. Of this,
the cause is obvious; the auricles were excited
to a degree of action incompatible with their
power; and this, in both cases, was urged so far
as to terminate in a total cessation of action.
You cannot however have overlooked the marked difference in point of severity of the symptoms in the first case. There you must have observed, that the disease was much more serious
than in the latter instance; but you must also
have been able to trace the cause of this difference, to the adhesion of the pericardium to both
the heart and neighbouring parts in the female,

while in the male, the heart, though altered in its texture, was still free from any attachment to the pericardium. The causes inducing a return of the paroxysm, you have seen to consist in whatever was capable of accelerating the action of the vascular system. This fact points directly to the plan of palliation, and shews, that in this as in most other affections of this organ, we must abstain from the use of stimuli. The patient, if he does more than merely vegetate, must take the responsibility on himself. Few, however, till too late, can be persuaded of the necessity of self-denial, and few therefore will submit to the privations which in this complaint are indispensably necessary. It is, however, the duty of the practitioner, to urge the matter with a warmth and zeal proportioned to its importance, and sometimes he may succeed; where he does not, he has the satisfaction of thinking that he had conscientiously discharged the trust reposed in him.

OBSERVATIONS

ON DISEASE OF THE CORONARY ARTERIES AND ON SYNCOPE ANGINOSA.

WE have just been considering the effects produced by ossification of the substance of the heart; let us next inquire into the consequences which result from loss of contractility of the coronary vessels. Frequent as we now find the cases of Syncope Anginosa to be, the discovery of the nature and causes of this disease, is comparatively of recent date. Examples of this affection, are indeed to be met with in some early authors, but the cases are considered anomalous, and no practical inference is deduced from them. To Drs. Hebberden, Jenner, and Parry, we owe most of our information respecting this most fatal complaint. After the very able treatise which Dr. Parry has published on this subject, very little can now be added to the information he has communicated regarding the pathology of Syncope Anginosa. By a series of well related cases, he establishes the regular history of the disease, and by fair induction from a series of accurately performed dissections, he confirms his opinions respecting the cause of this affection; which I think, he has incontrovertibly proved to originate from some organic læsion of the nutrient vessels of the heart. In all the patients who have died of Syncope Anginosa, where the body has been carefully examined, the coronary arteries have either been found ossified or cartilaginous. In some, as in the case of Mr. Bellamy, dissected by Mr. Paytherus, their inner surface has been found crusted over with a lymphatic exudation, " not " very dissimilar to the matter which forms on " the inside of the trachea in croup ;" and in most of them, the heart has been flabby and fat.

such a state of the arteries of the heart, must impair the function of that organ. It has been long known, that although the heart is always full of blood, yet it cannot appropriate to its own wants a single particle of fluid contained in its cavities. On the contrary, like every other part, it has peculiar vessels set apart for its nourishment. In health, when we excite the muscular system to more energetic action than usual, we increase the circulation in every part, so that to support this increased action, the heart and every other part has its power augmented. If, however, we call into vigorous action, a limb, round which, we have with a moderate degree of tightness applied a ligature, we find that then the member can only support its action for a very short time; for now its supply of energy and its expenditure, do not balance each other; consequently, it soon, from a deficiency of nervous influence and arterial blood, fails and sinks into a state of quiescence. A heart, the coronary vessels of which are cartilaginous or ossified, is in nearly a similar condition; it can, like the limb, be girt with a moderately tight ligature, discharge its functions so long as its action is moderate and equal. Increase however the action of the whole body, and along with the rest, that of the heart, and you will soon see exemplified, the truth of what has been said; with this difference, that as there is no interruption to the action of the cardiac nerves, the heart will be able to hold out a little longer than the limb.

IF a person walks fast, ascends a steep, or mounts a pair of stairs, the circulation in a state of health is hurried, and the heart is felt beating more frequently against the ribs than usual. If, however, a person, with the nutrient arteries of the heart diseased in such a way as to impede the progress of the blood along them, attempt to do the same, he finds, that the heart is sooner fatigued than the other parts are, which remain healthy. When, therefore, the coronary arteries are ossified, every agent capable of increasing the action of the heart, such as exercise, passion, and ardent spirits, must be a source of danger. Mr. Paytherus, in detailing the history of Mr. Bellamy's case, expressly states, that the first attack of serious disease in the heart, was brought on by drinking port wine to excess. The second, was "by walking up a field of easy ascent." Dr. Parry found, that in Mr. M. an attack was brought on by walking, on the 13th of April, 1797. On the 17th of the same month, by the same exciting cause, the complaint recurred, and on the 23d, the paroxysm which proved fatal, came on while walking. In a case which I attended, the attack was originally brought on by walking, and was regularly renewed as often as the patient attempted to ascend any steep place. In Mr. John Hunter, passion, or even mental agitation, were uniformly exciting causes of the renewal of the paroxysms. By these exciting causes, applied to a person in whom the nutrient arteries of the heart are diseased, an alarming fit of illness is induced. The heart is overpowered with blood accumulated in its cavities, it struggles with its load, but cannot free itself; the pulse pauses, then begins, is feeble, intermittent and faultering. The right ventricle ceases to propel the blood in due quantity into the pulmonary vessels; a sense of suffocation ensues, and an indescribable anxiety and oppression result from the accumulation of blood about the chest. The difficulty of breathing seems to a by-stander, and also to an inattentive patient, to be a most prominent symptom. When, however, he by a voluntary act, enlarges the size of the chest, he finds that he can as readily take in the air as formerly; but as the heart is not duly expelling the blood from its cavities, this fluid is not exposed to the influence of the air; consequently, as Mr. Home remarks, its presence or absence are of little moment. The feeling of suffocation most probably arises from the venous state of the blood, accumulated in the heart. Whether this supposition be correct or not, still it is of much consequence, that the real condition of the respiratory organs should be attended to: For if there be actual dyspnœa present, you may be certain, that the disease is either not Syncope Anginosa, or that it is a complicat:

ed case, conjoined with effusion into the chest, ossification of the valves, or asthma. Perhaps the most unequivocal evidence which has ever been brought forward to prove, that in Syncope Anginosa, there is no real difficulty in breathing, is the testimony of Mr. John Hunter, who was conscious, that during the fit, the respiratory function was perfectly suspended. He was certain of this fact, and believed, that unless he called into immediate action the voluntary respiratory muscles, he would soon die. With this view, he did voluntarily renew the process of breathing, but he did not find that either the pulse became more perceptible, or that the apparent want of breath was thereby removed. This quiescence of the heart, and the suspension of the breathing, are wise provisions of nature. They are the natural palliatives of this complaint. During this state of inactivity, the heart is slowly recovering its lost tone. They are in this disease, of the same value to the patient, that the forced, struggling, gasping respiration, is to a person who has malconformation of the heart. This must be enforced on your minds, for it is a lesson of importance. It is to be your guide in treating these diseases. It informs you, that in neither case ought the practitioner to interfere; the assistance he intends, may do more harm than good.

THE heart, assuredly, during the violence of the paroxysm, ceases to beat, but whether this be dependant on a state resembling paralysis, or on a spasmodic contraction of its fibres, it is perhaps not of much moment to ascertain. Mr. Home conjectures, that in Mr. Hunter, the heart was during the fit, in a state of spasmodic action; and he explains the pain which Mr. Hunter complained so much of, by supposing it to have been produced by the pressure of the cardiac nerves against the ossified arteries. The " stoppage of the pulse arose from a spasm upon " the heart, and in this state, the nerves were " probably pressed against the ossified arteries, " which may account for the excruciating pain " he felt at those times." I am afraid, however, that this is too mechanical an explanation of the mode of induction of this painful sensation; and I think it is hardly corroborated by any analogous fact in the animal œconomy. Do we ever, after the operation for aneurism, see the muscles in a state of rigid action, or when we apply the tourniquet only so tight as to impede the circulation; do we ever observe that the member is affected with spasm. In both cases, we witness an induction of an extreme degree of debility, and we hear the person complaining of an unusual painful feeling in the limb, but still its muscles are in a state of inactivity. If these be the phenomena resulting from a deficiency of arterial blood in the muscular system in general, why should the heart be an exception; we know that this organ is prin-

cipally composed of muscle, and we have therefore reason to believe, that it is regulated by
the same laws which govern other muscles.

IN the Syncope Anginosa, there is, in general,
along with the sense of suffocation, a feeling of
constriction about the chest, often accompanied
with a severe and pungent pain somewhere in
the thorax, and occasionally stretching into the
left arm. Frequently, the pain is most acutely
felt beneath the left mamma, and in some patients, the breast has even been painful when
pressed oh firmly. In other patients, the pain,
which, when present in the arm, is generally
seated about the implantation of the pectoral
muscles, extends over the shoulder, and down
to the elbow; and in the case of the Reverend
Mr. S. related by Dr. Parry, the pain " extend-
" ed into his right, as well as his left elbow."
In one also of Dr. Fothergill's patients, the
pain extended to both arms. In Mr. Hunter,
" the left arm could not bear to be touched;
" the least pressure on it giving pain." In
some of Dr. Parry's patients, the pain in the
arm was wanting, and in one which came under my care, the person never had any uneasy
sensation about the arms. This pain in the
arm or arms, is frequently absent, and its presence is no more to be depended on as pathognomonic of this complaint, than the start-
ing of the patient from his sleep, terrified with
some awful dream, is to be looked on as a sure

sign of water in the chest. In the early part of the disease, the pulse is not so much affect- ed as one would expect; neither is the cessa- tion from action in the heart, so complete as af- terward; and the duration and severity of the pa- roxysm, are mitigated by refraining from a per- severance in the exciting cause which brought on the attack. If, however, the person attempts to brave the disease, and with that view per- sists in walking, for example, after the accession of the fit, he will soon fall into a state of actual syncope, and will remain in that condition for a longer or shorter time, according to the stage of the disease, and extent of operation of the exciting cause. After remaining for some time in a state of quiescence, wind is in general ex- pelled from the stomach. The heart then gra- dually resumes its languid and imbecile mode of acting. Indeed, it always presents more the semblance than the reality of action; its move- ments are always without energy, and trivial causes are sufficient to derange its function.

IN the advanced period of Syncope Anginosa, the stomach is frequently morbidly affected; be- coming unusually irritable, and rejecting what- ever is swallowed. Now the paroxysms, which in the incipient stage of the disease, were only brought on by walking up a steep, by mounting stairs, or by walking or riding against the wind, or by gusts of passion, or by mental anxiety, or by hard drinking, are induced by walking even

slowly over level ground; by the usual exertions of speaking, swallowing, or discharging
the different excretions; or they even return
periodically, as Dr. Parry observes, " from two
" to four o'clock in the morning, without any
" previous exertion, or obvious cause. The
" paroxysms now also become more violent,
" and do not so readily recede. During the
" fit, the pulse sinks in a greater degree, the
" face and extremities become pale, and bathed
" in a cold sweat, and for a while, perhaps the
" patient is deprived of the power of sense and
" voluntary motion. At length, after the dis-
" ease has recurred more or less frequently,
" sometimes during a space of many years,
" which admit of the patient's death: from a
" variety of other causes, a more violent attack
" of the nature which I have just described,
" puts a sudden period to his existence." He
dies at last, after having many times over, suffered all the agonies of dissolution; for this is a
complaint, in which, during the fit, there are
the most overwhelming sensations, and an apprehension of instant death.

IT was asserted by many, previous to the
time that Dr. Parry wrote, that in this disease,
there was palpitation of the heart. This author
justly observes, that in the real Syncope Anginosa, there never is palpitation, and the reason
is obvious. When treating of chronic inflammation of the heart, and adhesion of the pericar-

dium, I endeavoured to shew, that palpitation is a mere irregularity in the natural mode of acting, and therefore that it rarely can attend any serious organic lesion of the heart. In the Syncope Anginosa, it is obvious, that it never can be present; for the essence of this complaint consists in a reduction of the action of the heart, which state, we know to be incompatible with palpitation.

THIS is a disease, which may, by proper attention to regularity in diet, and moderation in drinking, be generally prevented from proceeding, at least to an alarming extent. The patient must refrain from violent exercise, must eat nothing but the lightest and most digestible food, and must chiefly employ a vegetable diet, using, however, only such vegetables as have least tendency to produce flatulence. He must also refrain from fermented fluids, and as much as possible, from the use of wine: he must be careful, by gentle laxatives, and regular exercise on horseback, where his circumstances will permit, to keep the bowels regular. Whenever he perceives any tendency to plenitude in the vascular system, he must rigidly adhere to an antiphlogistic regimen, and use occasionally such quantity of the submuriat of mercury, conjoined with some aromatic, as canella alba, ginger, cardamom seeds, or cassia, as shall produce a free alvine discharge.

DURING the paroxysm, we are to lay the pa-

tient in a recumbent posture, and if there be a
great degree of oppression and constriction
about the chest, we are even, although the pulse
be faultering and weak, to detract a few ounces
of blood ; for in some cases we find, that the
heart is prevented from beginning to act again,
by the blood with which it is overloaded.   In
this situation of matters, by opening the jugular vein, and gently pressing on the chest, we
endeavour to expel a portion of blood from the
right side of the heart, for precisely the same
reason that we sometimes use the lancet in
suspended animation.   Indeed, in a paroxysm
of Angina Pectoris, we are to proceed nearly
on the same principle which would guide us, if
called to a person who was in a state of asphyxia, from submersion in water.   Our decided object must be, to allow the exhausted
heart slowly to recover its lost energy.   We
are, where the person is in a state of actual
syncope, to bathe the forehead and breast with
the coldest water we can procure ; and when
the breathing begins, when the person, after
long intervals, fetches a deep convulsive sigh,
and is just able to open his eyes, we may hold
ammonia to the nose, or we may convey into
the stomach, a small portion of some aromatic
powder or water.   These we employ to facilitate the expulsion of wind from the stomach,
which seldom fails to relieve the patient.
Where however, the cessation of vital action

is very complete, and continues long, we ought to inflate the lungs, and pass electric shocks through the chest: the practitioner ought never, if the death has been sudden, and the person not very far advanced in life, to despair of success, till he has unequivocal signs of real death. But while the person is either in a state of actual fainting, or just recovering from this condition, let the practitioner beware of the exhibition of stimuli, with the view of rousing the patient. By these, the heart just beginning to emerge from its temporary cessation of function, will indeed, be made for a short time to shew signs of returning animation, but the hope is delusive; for speedily it falls into its former state, from which no stimulant, however powerful, can again recal it. We have known some surgeons, from the contemplation of the deep prostration of strength, administer wine and cordials; but in no case, which has come to our knowledge, have these ever proved beneficial.

WE have seen two persons, and one of these, a fine young girl not more than sixteen years of age, lose their lives, from their friends, who were alarmed at seeing them lying inanimate, and their countenances white as paper, having poured stimulants into the stomach: They with a good intention, forced wine down the throat of one, and whisky down that of the other; and the consequence was, that in both,

the pulse began to beat, it fluttered, however, and
sometimes paused; the heart resumed its action,
but it never became in any degree regular; the
whole system discharged its functions in a discordant manner; and in a few days both the patients died.   When we are endeavouring to recover a person who has been drowned, after we
get a certain length, gentle stimuli introduced
into the stomach are highly beneficial, but in
Syncope Anginosa, I would dread their employment in any stage; and in the more advanced
stages, they must be doubly pernicious.   In the
case of Mr. Hunter, recourse was had " to the
" camphorated julep, both at the commence-
" ment of the spasm, and while it was on him,
" but, he obtained no relief.   He tried Hoff-
" man's anodyne liquor, in the dose of a tea
" spoonful, and not finding it answer alone,
" joined to it the camphorated julep; but the
" spasms seemed to be more violent.   One night
" he took twenty drops of Thebiac tincture,
" which made his head confused all the follow-
" ing day, but did not at all abate the spasms.
" As he had not drunk wine for four or five
" years, he was advised to try it, which he com-
" plied with; but found the spasms more readily
" brought on after using it, than on those days
" in which he drank none, and they were al-
" ways more readily produced after eating a
" hearty meal."   From this statement, which is
given by Mr. E. Home, it is evident, that sti-

muli were not attended with any good effect in
Mr. Hunter's complaint: they produced precisely the consequences which, reasoning *a priori* might have been expected from their employment, in a person in whom the nutrient
arteries of the heart were diseased. In the case
of Mr. M. detailed by Dr. Parry, it is mentioned, that " his limbs were now rubbed with warm
" flannels, his feet were bathed in hot water,
" and two glasses of brandy were gradually
" given him; he swallowed it without difficulty,
" and said, that it felt warm in his stomach,
" but it produced no eructation; after a quar-
" ter of an hour, he answered us, that he was
" less faint, though neither the pulse grew
" stronger, nor the skin warmer, or more dry,
" at half past four." It was at four o'clock,
that Dr. Parry saw him, " he complained that
" the pain again affected his heart, across the
" middle of the sternum."

This gentleman became weaker, and " ceas-
" ed to answer questions, breathed only at in-
" tervals, and at five o'clock, without a groan,
" or convulsion, expired." It would be injustice to Dr. Parry, not to mention the remark
which he afterwards makes on this case, and on
the use of stimulants in this disease. " In ca-
" ses of such debility and death-like coldness,
" it is natural to have recourse to cordials of
" various kinds; I have however related the
" evident mischief arising from their use, in

" the case of Sir E. W. and in that of my pa-
" tient Mr. M.; the reader has seen, that no
" benefit was derived from the exhibition of
" four or five ounces of pure brandy. On the
" whole, it seems to me, that during the parox-
" ysms, stimulants can be safely taken, only as
" far as they may be required to remove flatu-
" lency from the stomach, or at least, that their
" use should be deferred to that period, when
" after the failure of the other means already
" suggested, the pulse is not at all, or scarcely
" to be felt."   Dr. Parry is evidently averse to
the employment of cordials or wine, but still he
has conceded too much to the doctrines of the
day, and has permitted the use of stimuli, at
the very moment, when, if they produce any
effect, it must be a most pernicious one. If a
practitioner were called to a person who had a
limb frost-bitten, cold, livid, and motionless, he
would not dip it in pretty hot water. On the
contrary, he would apply a substance only
a little hotter than the member itself, and would
very gently stimulate the torpid parts. In Syncope Anginosa, if all the means which have
been " already suggested," have been employed, and if still, " the pulse is not at all, or
" scarcely to be felt;" is it probable, that brandy
or wine will do more than merely rouse the
system, into an inefficient and destructive action? It would be productive of precisely the
same effects on the system at large, that plung-

ing a frost-bitten limb into hot water, would have on the individual member. In Angina Pectoris, we must, even when foiled for a length of time, still persist in the means I have formerly pointed out; and we are at all times to remember, that we shall generally gain more by the use of bleeding, than by the exhibition of stimuli. The strongest stimulus we ought to employ, is electric sparks passed through the chest, and friction of the limbs with hot flannels, or with stimulating embrocations. If these, absolute rest, and lying in a recumbent posture fail, we can have very little hope of success from any other plan.

In those who are subject to Syncope Anginosa, we must, where there is torpidity of the stomach or bowels, or irregular action of the chylopoietic organs, endeavour to remove these adventitious diseases, before we can reasonably expect to palliate the affection of the heart. In many cases, the paroxysms of Angina Pectoris have been brought on, and perpetuated by torpidity of the bowels. In such cases, we must use bitters, conjoined with aromatics and laxatives; and I have found nothing answer better than powders composed of colomba, canella alba and aloes, or of cascarilla and rhubarb. Where the sleep is interrupted, we may, with safety, employ extract of hyoscyamus as an anodyne.

BEFORE concluding the history of Syncope

Anginosa, I may detail the particulars of a case which I had an opportunity of attending during a part of the patient's illness, and which is, in some respects, an interesting one. I had not occasion to see this gentleman Mr. G. in the early stage of his complaint, but I learned from himself, that he was above forty years of age: that about four years before, he had, while walking, been attacked with a violent pain in the breast, accompanied with constriction of the chest, and sense of suffocation. According to his statement, there had never been any pain stretching into the arms, neither were the morbid sensations in the thorax at first very acute; they were, however, so severe as to compel him to stand still for a little, when they gradually wore off. He could walk readily and quickly on level ground, without any attack; and he could ride very briskly on horseback, without exciting a paroxysm, except when the wind blew strongly in his face. After he had continued for some time in this state, he became gradually much worse; he lost his appetite, his feet became œdematous, he started often from his sleep, he could not breathe except with great difficulty; but he found that the respiratory process was carried on most easily when in a semi-erect posture: his hands also swelled, his urine was scanty, and high coloured, and he was tormented with thirst. His medical attendants, from a persuasion of the most prominent symptoms being produced by effusion into the chest, prescribed squills, digitalis, and various other diuretics, but none of them had a good effect; under their use, he became daily worse. At last from popular report, he learned the virtues of an infusion of broom tops, and was anxious to try this remedy; his friends urged him to it, his medical attendants were willing to try any thing: he persevered for a few weeks in the use of this remedy, and found, that during its employment, the quantity of his urine was enormously increased; the swellings in his limbs were completely removed, and the urgent symptoms of disease disappeared. He never, however, completely recovered from his complaints, but he got so well, that he married only a few months before his death. At the time of his marriage, he was obliged to refrain from walking much, on account of it exciting the pain in the region of the heart, and the sense of suffocation. In other respects, he was quite healthy; he had a good appetite, his bowels were regular, his urine was passed in proper quantity, and he could lie equally well on both sides, and on his back.

ABOUT five or six months after his marriage, I was consulted with respect to his complaint. On enquiring how he was affected, he informed me, that if he attempted to walk up even a very easy ascent which led to his house, he felt a most acute pain in the chest, just under the left breast; that his breathing was very difficult, that he was becoming worse every day; for now he was frequently awaked with a sense of load and oppression in the thorax, and that this and the dyspnœa continued till he raised himself erect. I found, although in the beginning of this illness, there had been no real difficulty in breathing, that yet, when I attended him, there was actual dyspnœa; he was harassed with a short, hard, husky cough, accompanied with slight expectoration of tough mucus; his urine was scanty, and his limbs and scrotum œdematous. The legs were so enormously swelled, that he could not even get on a pair of very wide boots. Yet even at this stage of the disease, to a superficial observer, he seemed, excepting the clumsiness of his limbs, and the huge size of the scrotum, to be in perfect health. He was a big muscular man, with considerable colour in his face; yet, on looking narrowly, one could easily see that his complexion was not a healthy one : the red was circumscribed in his cheek, and was not of the bright carnation; it had a shade of the purple in it, and his lips were of a dusky colour. Notwithstanding his apparent strength, he was easily fatigued, and he complained bitterly of the bad effect which frosty weather had on him. His appetite was tolerably good, but his bowels were very torpid, and his pulse which generally ranged from about 95 to 105, had a very unpleasant feel; it was irregular, and appeared oppressed; yet, by slight exercise, it became excessively feeble, and the patient felt that anguish in the chest, and failure of the function of the heart, attendant on a diseased state of the coronary arteries.

CONSIDERING all circumstances, I had no hope of effecting a cure. As the dropsical symptoms were the most prominent and distressing; and as the cough seemed to be produced by effusion into the chest, I ordered him to take a mixture containing tincture of digitalis, ammoniated tincture of opium and peppermint water; and I also prescribed the occasional use of laxatives. He persisted for a time in the use of these; but although the cough was abated, and he could rest more comfortably during the night, still the swelling of his limbs rather increased. At last, they ceased to have any good effect; he then tried infusion of digitalis, powder of digitalis and squills, in various forms and combinations, but all without benefit. In short, every diuretic that could be suggested, and even broom tea was successively tried, but still the œdema increased. Almost no urine was passed; he could not for a minute lie in the recumbent posture, without dread of instant suffocation; yet his appetite was pretty good, and his pulse was even fuller, and more oppressed than before, and his countenance was more of the purple hue. His mind however was still serene, and he was cheerful, for he dreaded no

danger; he thought his complaint more teazing than serious. As by this time, his limbs
and scrotum were distended even to bursting;
and his bowels had become again exceedingly torpid, he was directed to take ʒviij. of the
super-tartrite of potass every evening. He
did so, with the effect of rendering brisker the
intestinal action, but there was no reduction
of the swellings, nor augmentation of the urine.
He was next persuaded by one of his friends, to
try gin toddy; he daily for two days, took a few
glasses of it, and found that the quantity of his
urine was increased, but he found himself more
restless and oppressed after it, and the œdema
had gained so much on him, that he was now
unable to bear the pressure of the rollers about
his legs. As he was always becoming worse in
place of better, his friends were anxious to have
the water drawn off by punctures, but this I
refused to do; fearing, that in the distended
and weakened state of the skin, almost instant
gangrene would exhaust the strength. On this
account, another practitioner of great respect-
ability, and professional information was desired
to attend. He tried diuretics, but found them of
no advantage; he therefore made a few punctures about the ankles, the fluid readily drained
off, but next day the wounds became black and
sphacelated, and in a few hours, without any return of the affection of the heart, the patient
died.

ANXIOUS as I was to ascertain the state of the heart and vessels, still as I had not been in attendance till the last, I could not request permission to do so, and the practitioner who did see him, never proposed any examination of the body. We cannot therefore be completely certain, that this affection was in reality the consequence of disease in the nutrient vessels of the heart; and some may even be inclined to believe, from the presence of actual dyspnœa, that it had rather been the effect of rigid valves. From reviewing the history and progress of the complaint, I am convinced that it was a case of Syncope Anginosa. In the early stage of the disease, the patient had no real difficulty in breathing; that symptom only made its appearance after there were evident marks of effusion into the chest; and further, by the use of diuretics, especially the infusion of broom, you would observe, that the patient had the difficulty in breathing completely removed, but still the affection of the heart remained unaltered; a fact which proves, that the dyspnœa had been induced not by the state of the heart, but by the pressure on the lungs. If we add to these, that the difficulty in breathing was permanent, we shall have little doubt remaining as to the source of dyspnœa.

THIS case is, in my apprehension, valuable on another account; for it shews, that notwithstanding the opinion of some, that plethora is hardly compatible with such a disease of the heart; there was in this patient, a plethoric state of the sanguiferous system. From the state of the pulse, had there been no affection of the heart, I would never have hesitated about the propriety of using the lancet; and even, notwithstanding the existence of the disease of the heart, had I been acquainted at the time this case occurred, with the observations of Grapengiessir, I would have tried the effect of abstracting a small quantity of blood. A review of Grapengiessir's book, may be found in the Annals of Medicine for 1798. I had a recollection of having somewhere read of the cure of a certain variety of dropsy, by venesection; but I could not remember where I had seen it, till at last, I met accidentally with the review of Dr. Grapengiessir's book, in Dr. Duncan's Annals of Medicine for the year 1798. Dr. Duncan, jun. very politely sent me the essay for examination. It is in so far as I know, the first attempt to prove by unbiassed reasoning, that dropsy frequently requires for its cure, the use of the lancet. In the works of both ancient and modern writers, on the practice of medicine, cases are indeed related of the cure of dropsy by venesection; and there are few practitioners who do not know that detraction of blood is the best diuretic, where serous effusion had been brought on in young people, by exposure to cold. Few, however, knew the principle on which they proceed-

ed, and none professedly treated on this subject
before Dr. Grapengiessir, who, in the year
1795, published an essay, entitled " *Dissertatio
Medica de Hydrope Plethorico*." In this essay,
he proves by a review of the opinions of authors,
and by the phenomena presented by the disease,
that the plethoric dropsy assumes two forms;
one in which it is characterized by the symptoms which indicate the presence of plenitude;
another, in which these symptoms are obscure
and indistinct; or, as Mr. Watt would suppose, in
which there was a greater quantity of blood in the
vessels than the lungs are capable of purifying.

THE one species he calls the Hydrops Plethoricus Acutus; the other the Hydrops Plethoricus
Chronicus. In the schools, however, debility is
so universally taught to be the cause of serous
effusion, that few even when they do see cases
evidently complicated, with an inflammatory
diathesis, can so far divest themselves of preju-
dices early imbibed, as to view the disease in
its true colour; or, if they do reluctantly yield
their assent to the fact, that dropsy may be complicated with plethora, yet they are little inclined to push the depleting system to its due
extent. Most practitioners must have had occasion to witness the truth of Dr. Grapengeissir's remarks, and most, if inclined, might recollect cases in which the whole list of diuretics were employed in vain; nay, sometimes as
in the case of Mr. G. with an obvious aggravation of the disease. Indeed, Dr. Grapengeissir

remarks, that in the Hydrops Plethoricus, purgatives and diuretics exasperate the symptoms; and he states, that detraction of blood will alone save the person, and here the blood exhibits the buffy crust. Had I seen these observations, or at least, had I fully recollected them, when this case came under my care, I would not have pushed the use of the diuretics and purgatives to the extent I did; and had I not found the dropsy complicated with Angina Pectoris, a disease, which in the advanced stage, we have been taught to view as almost incompatible with Plethora, I would on account even of the oppression of the pulse, have employed the lancet. From the use of this I was however deterred, by observing the excessive feebleness of the pulse induced by exercise, although you will find this to be a very fallacious symptom. For owing to the inactivity of the heart, the blood could not be duly propelled into the vascular system; and thus, although Plethora did exist, it was not characterised by the usual marks of that condition, nor can it be so when the nutrient vessels of the heart are ossified. Had I reflected on this, I would not, from the feebleness of the pulse induced by exertion, have been dissuaded from bleeding, but would have tried the effect, in the first instance, of taking away only a very small quantity of blood; and this I am now satisfied, is the practice which ought to have been followed. I was, however, for the reasons I have already stated, led to refrain from bleeding, and I must confess, that I had an expectation of the same event following in this second attack, as in the former. When he was formerly ill, he had, as when under my care, tried every diuretic which could be thought of, but no alteration for the better had been produced. At last, when he was sinking, the employment of an empirical potion of broom tea, removed the dropsical symptoms. In the attack during which I attended him, I trusted, that when his strength was more reduced, either the digitalis, or some other remedy of this kind, would have produced a free discharge of urine; nor was this a hope, which we do not frequently see realized. We often find, that in the early stage of dropsy, while the patients are, as Dr. Withering observes, robust, and of firm fibre, that the diuretics make no impression, but that when the strength is more wasted, the very same medicines cure the disease. In the case of Mr. G. had the lancet been used, there is a probability that the system would have been brought into such a state, as to have permitted the diuretics to produce their proper effect, or perhaps, by the continuance of the disease, the same end might have been accomplished; for I do not think, that of itself, the affection of the heart had advanced so far as to have proved fatal. The death was unquestionably accelerated by the punctures into the limbs.

OBSERVATIONS

ON THE EFFECTS RESULTING FROM CHANGE OF
STRUCTURE OF THE VALVES OF THE HEART AND
LARGE ARTERIES.

CHANGE of structure of the substance of the
heart, is not by any means so frequent an occurrence, as alteration in the texture of the
Valves. We are not, however, in every case,
where after death, we find these appendages
opaque, to conclude, that this change from the
healthy transparent state, shall have been accompanied with a correspondent alteration in
the function. The auricular valves are more
rarely affected than the arterial ones, and those
on the right side, are less subject to disease than
those on the left. Columbus saw the auricular
valves ossified; and in such cases, the arterial
ones are generally at the same time in a morbid
state. As the pulmonic valves are both more
rarely affected than the aortic; and at the same
time, as they are, when diseased, productive of
less perfectly marked symptoms, we know less
of the effects produced by disease of the one,
than we do of the other. From what we have
learnt respecting disease in the pulmonary valves,
it would appear, that when the blood is obstructed in its passage to the lungs, the per-

son is generally emaciated, of a sallow complexion, constantly labouring under a load and oppression about the breast; a struggling about the chest, a feeling of constriction in the thorax, and the symptoms of dilatation of the right side of the heart; and in the end, they are carried off by reiterated attacks of syncope and dropsical effusions. These are the symptoms which most frequently result from the passage of the blood into the lungs being obstructed. When the aortic valves are thickened, indurated, and encroach on the canal of the vessel, we find that there is, on using exercise, a greater or less difficulty of breathing brought on; sometimes attended with expectoration of a serous bloody fluid, or at other times, followed by a torrent of frothy blood from the trachea. The pulse is intermitting and variable, pretty regular when the person is at rest, but discordant, and not equally frequent with the contraction of the heart, when the person is fatigued. There is often palpitation of the heart, or rather an irregularity of action, bearing some resemblance to it; there is an oppression about the chest, accompanied often with pungent pain in the region of the heart, and severe dyspnœa; and in very urgent cases, the person, toward the close of life, becomes dark on the surface, and dies dropsical. Ossification, or induration of the mitral valve, is productive of nearly the same effects, as arise from obstruction at the

mouth of the aorta. To Dr. Brown, I am indebted for the case of the boy Warnoch, who
died in the Edinburgh hospital. This patient's
case was taken on the 27th of November. " He
" has pain, shooting from the point of the ster-
" num, along both sides to the spine, nearly in
" the direction of the attachment of the dia-
" phragm; frequently he has violent palpita-
" tion, pulse 123, small and feeble; reiterated
" fits of coughing, preventing him from sleep-
" ing, and attended with copious and free bloody
" expectoration; dyspnœa, nausea and vomit-
" ing, especially after his meals; thirst great,
" tongue clean and moist; urine scanty and
" high coloured, fluctuation in the abdomen,
" and general œdema."

" AT a remote period, he had cough, pain of
" breast, of the stomach, and vomiting. The
" dropsical symptoms first made their appear-
" ance four months ago, at which time he came
" into the hospital, under the care of Dr. Ha-
" milton, by whose prescriptions he was soon
" so much relieved, that he left the house; he
" had not however been long away, when the
" symptoms returned. It may be proper to
" add, that he has been employed in a glass-
" work, where he was subjected to frequent
" changes of temperature."

ON the 28th, the report is, " a bad night,
" breathing quick and laborious, countenance
" inflated, severe headach, pulse extremely
" quick; frequent cough, with bloody expec-

" toration; three natural stools, urine high co-
" loured, and deposits much sediment."

A BLISTER was applied over the sternum, and
he was directed to take a mixture with ether.

ON the 29th, " a bad night, somewhat re-
" lieved to-day ; lips less livid, coughs less, fre-
" quent nausea."

HE was this day directed to continue the
ether, and in addition, a squill mixture and
four ounces of wine, were prescribed to be taken
daily.

30th, " Worse in all respects; dyspnœa ex-
" treme, and skin cold;" a scruple of ether was
desired to be taken immediately.

DECEMBER 1st, he died.

DISSECTION. " The abdomen and thorax,
" both contained a quantity of yellow serum ;
" the anterior part of the pericardium, at its
" junction with the diaphragm, as well as the
" diaphragm itself, were of a deep red colour,
" and fleshy appearance; and from both these
" parts, a number of processes were sent off in-
" to the cavity of the chest; some joining the
" lungs to the pericardium, some binding them
" to the diaphragm, the lungs themselves were
" darker coloured than usual, and more solid,
" and they contained bloody mucus.

" BETWEEN the pericardium and heart, a
" quantity of yellow serum was lodged; the
" heart itself was enlarged, more especially the
" right auricle and ventricle, which were both

" distended, with dark coloured but fluid blood.
" The parietes of the right ventricle were thicker
" than usual, and the valves on this side were per-
" fectly sound; in the left ventricle, the mitral
" valve was much thickened and contracted;
" the chordæ tendineæ, were very short and al-
" most as thick as crow quills; and the colum-
" næ carneæ were uncommonly large, though
" diminished in length; the passage from the
" auricle to the ventricle was very much con-
" tracted; the projecting columnæ carneæ form-
" ing there a close net work."

THIS case corroborates the general account
which has been given, and it shews, as indeed
many other cases do, the fallacy of Dr. Parry's
statement, that it is generally the cavity immediately before the obstructed part which is dilated. Here it is expressly stated, that it was
the right side of the heart which was chiefly
dilated ; but the history of this person requires
to be still further attended to, for the morbid
phenomena illustrate a point often met with.
You have had occasion to observe, that Dr.
Brown says, " the parietes of the right ventricle
" were thicker than usual." This I would particularly call your attention to, for it is a fact
which we could corroborate, by several analogous cases. It proves, that in proportion to
the resistance offered to the passage of the
blood, the circulating powers have their strength
augmented. This is a position diametrically

opposite to the inference Dr. Parry has been led to draw from the review of his cases. This author concludes, that in fourteen only out of ninety-two cases, which he has examined in the works of authors, direct mention is not made of some circumstance, from which it may justly be presumed, that the expulsory power of the heart, comparatively with the quantity of blood to be expelled, was considerably diminished.

ANOTHER point in the history of the symptoms, was very clearly elucidated by the dissection. I allude to the pain following the course of the attachment of the diaphragm. On the examination, the sequelæ of inflammation were obvious, all along the pained tract.

THE following very valuable case, to which, when treating of the imperfect arterialization of the blood, I had occasion to refer, has been furnished me by my friend Dr. Balmanno. The symptoms and morbid phenomena are detailed with great truth and accuracy; and you will learn from the perusal of this history, that where the evacuation of blood is very profuse, the bronchial cells have so little air admitted into them, as not to change the venous colour of the blood, which, as we shall afterward see, is generally, when discharged from the trachea, florid and frothy. In almost every other respect, this case corroborates the detail already given.

" A MAN aged thirty, tall, slender, and of a

" constitution originally delicate, had from
" his earliest remembrance, been subject to
" some degree of dyspnœa, and to frequent at-
" tacks of palpitation.

" AT the age of twenty-one, in consequence
" of very close application to his business, in
" the course of which, he had frequently occa-
" sion to use the blow-pipe, his health was
" much impaired. The dyspnœa and palpita-
" tion became unusually distressing. During a
" short journey on foot, he was seized with a
" fit of coughing, and expectorated about a
" pound of blood. After having been for three
" months subject to occasional hæmoptysis, he
" gradually recovered his usual infirm state of
" health.

" TWO years after the expectoration of blood
" had ceased, the dyspnœa and palpitation
" without any very obvious occasional cause,
" became more urgent than ever; I then at-
" tended him for the first time.

" AT my first visit, I found him sitting, in-
" clined forwards on a table furnished with pil-
" lows; his respiration was laborious, short and
" gasping; he had a short cough, with scarcely
" any expectoration; his pulse very often in-
" termitted, and was so frequent, irregular,
" small and feeble, that it could not be num-
" bered; the action of the heart was also irre-
" gular, and so violent, as visibly to agitate the
" whole body; it was felt very strong in the

" epigastrium, and on the right side of the ster-
" num; it communicated to the hand, some-
" thing like the sensation of a tumbling mo-
" tion. I was not sensible of any jarring, gush-
" ing, or tremor. The apex of the heart beat
" considerably lower than usual; he perspired
" profusely; there was a great degree of ana-
" sarca of the limbs, and pretty general pitting
" on pressure, all over the body; the urine
" was much diminished; the lips were livid,
" and the rest of the face somewhat of the
" same hue, and a little turgid. There seemed
" to be some degree of stupor.

" MR. TOWERS, surgeon, who also attended
" the patient, agreed with me in judging the
" case to be almost hopeless; yet we determin-
" ed to try the effect of diuretics; for it appear-
" ed to us, that the dyspnœa might partly pro-
" ceed from aqueous effusion into the breast; ac-
" cordingly, the squill was prescribed, and the
" breast at the same time was blistered. On
" the following day, our patient was easier, and
" the squill operating powerfully as a diuretic.
" In the course of two or three days, there was
" an evident remission of urgent symptoms.
" Under the use of this medicine, the dyspnœa
" and palpitation gradually abated, and the
" anasarca subsided. During his convalescence,
" some bitters, tonics, and occasionally, laxa-
" tives were used.

" FOR seven years, he continued in a weak

" languid state. He has assured me, that he was
" at times quite free from any sense of the ac-
" tion of the heart ; but the slightest exertion
" of the body, or agitation of the mind, produ-
" ced palpitation, dyspnœa and copious sweat.
" His pulse, even in his best state of health,
" was from 90 to 100, very irregular both in
" strength and frequency, and always inter-
" mittent ; the heart usually gave a double
" throb for each pulsation at the wrist, and
" its action was violent, while the pulse was
" weak ; his sleep was short and disturbed.
" When in bed, he lay on his back, supported
" by pillows, so as to be nearly half erect ; he
" never could lie in the horizontal posture, nor
" on either side. He did not complain of any fix-
" ed pain in the breast, or of any uneasiness of
" the left arm. The lividity of the face, and
" œdema of the ankles, never entirely left him.

" ABOUT the end of February last, he re-
" quested that I would again visit him ; he com-
" plained of great weakness, and of an increase
" of all his usual ailments ; his pulse was about
" 120, very small and weak ; his urine was di-
" minished ; the anasarca of the lower extremi-
" ties was much increased, and he was costive. I
" ordered him to take as much Sup. Tart. Potas.
" daily, as to keep the belly open ; to use a
" milk diet, and if he should feel a desire for a
" cordial, to take a little weak gin punch. A
" week after I had prescribed as above, I was

" again requested to visit him; the Sup. Tart.
" Potass. had been taken in such quantity, as to
" produce purging, and after he had given up
" the use of it, he still had three or four loose
" stools daily; he was much weaker; com-
" plained of sickness, and was sometimes distres-
" sed with vomiting; all the other symptoms were
" greatly aggravated. The diarrhea was soon
" checked by astringents with opium; the sick-
" ness and vomiting ceased after a few doses
" of columbo.

" THE squill had formerly been most useful
" in removing the dropsical symptoms; but
" now, neither this, digitalis, nor any other
" medicine, increased the urine, or relieved the
" dyspnœa; and as diuretics either affected the
" bowels or occasioned nausea, I soon gave up
" the use of them. As he now complained of
" acute pain in the right side of the breast, a
" blister was applied to the part with benefit, the
" dyspnœa was occasionally relieved by ether.
" This symptom became so urgent, that he
" could no longer recline in bed, but was oblig-
" ed to sit constantly either erect, or inclined
" forwards, according as suffocation or syncope
" threatened most. About the same time he
" began to spit up some blood; the blood which
" he expectorated, was sometimes coagulated,
" but when most abundant, generally fluid, and
" always of a dark colour; the anasarca con-
" tinued to increase; the skin and eyes became

" tinged, of a deep yellow colour, approaching
" to brown ; he was much troubled with flatus.
" The expectoration of blood having continued
" to occur occasionally for eight days, suddenly
" became more frequent and profuse; the pulse
" was now fluttering and extremely small and
" feeble. At one time it ceased altogether, but
" could again be felt after copious expectora-
" tion. The extremities became cold and very
" livid. Soon after this occurrence, he died, ap-
" parently as much from suffocation, as from
" gradual exhaustion.

" THE action of the heart, some time before
" death, was said to be audible, but to me it
" never seemed so strong during this last illness,
" as when I first attended him, neither was the
" dyspnœa permanently so urgent; some relief
" being usually obtained from expectoration,
" he was quite free from stupor, and perfectly
" sensible, almost until he expired."

" DISSECTION. This was performed in the
" presence, and with the assistance of my friend
" Dr. Brown.

" THE heart was very large, the right auri-
" cle was dilated to an enormous size, and fully
" distended with fluid blood; it extended much
" farther than usual toward the right side of
" the thorax; when viewed *in situ*, it almost en-
" tirely concealed the other parts of the heart;
" the venæ cavæ and pulmonary artery were
" also much dilated. In the latter, there was
" a polypus, or rather coagulum.

" THE left auricle contained a concretion
" larger than a pigeon's egg; this substance
" was of an irregular round form, it appeared
" as if it had been composed of several portions
" forcibly pressed together; it was of firm con-
" sistence, but somewhat friable, and of gra-
" nular structure; it was covered by a distinct
" membrane, and adhered firmly to the side of
" the cavity, which was every where lined with
" lymphatic incrustation, and in many places
" ossified.

" A CIRCULAR membrane occupied the place
" of the mitral valve; the only aperture for the
" transmission of blood from the auricle into
" the ventricle, was a small perforation, near
" the centre of the membrane. This perforation
" was of an oval form, and not large enough to
" allow the little finger to pass through it.   It
" had a regular, well defined, and somewhat
" thickened margin. The chordæ tendineæ were
" implanted irregularly over the whole lower
" surface of this septum, so as to retain the
" membrane constantly drawn somewhat down-
" wards into a conical form.   The ductus ar-
" teriosus and foramen ovale, were, as usual,
" impervious; the aorta was natural.

" THE lungs on the left side, adhered to the
" fore part of the thorax; on the right, the ad-
" hesion was intimate and extensive; no tuber-
" cles, nor any appearance of pus, could be de-
" tected; nor was it evident that there had been

" any effusion into the parenchyma. On inci-
" sion, the blood flowed much more abundantly
" than usual, especially from the right lung;
" all the ramifications of the bronchiæ, into
" which we cut, were either filled or smeared
" with blood.

" THERE was but little aqueous fluid in the
" pericardium, and scarcely any, either in the
" cavity of the thorax, or in that of the abdo-
" men.

" THE liver was of natural size, but evident-
" ly much indurated."

WE find in Lieutaud's 563d Observation, a
case, where the aorta was obstructed very near
to the heart, probably from a thickening and
induration of its valves. It is only mentioned,
that a middle aged man, had, for many years
been subject to palpitation of the heart, and that
for the last six months of his life, the pulse had
been almost imperceptible.

IF the history of the symptoms be related
with a truly laconic brevity, that of the dissection is no less so; " *Repertum fuit callum ad*
" *osseam duritiem accedens in arteria magna*
" *loco cordi proximo.*"

IN another case related by Willis, the ligamentous zone which connects the aorta to the
heart, was gritty, and the opening from the ventricle into the large artery, was a mere slit,
" *ejusque ostium rimæ instar angustatum.*" The
narration of the concomitant symptoms of this

deviation from the usual structure, is exceedingly imperfect; "*crebros cordis palpitationis insultus patiebatur; et demum quotidiano vomitu, virium languore, aliisque symtomatibus extinctus erat.*" In this case a symptom is mentioned, which is by no means unfrequent in many diseases of the heart, I mean the vomiting. In one or two cases of obstruction about the root of the aorta we have seen this a most distressing symptom. The 412th OBSERVAT. related by Riverius, illustrates well the effect of impediment to the circulation of the blood from the ventricle into the aorta. This patient had palpitation of the heart, an unequal pulse, in the end, almost imperceptible; difficulty in breathing, amounting under certain circumstances to a threatening of suffocation. Bloody expectoration, and œdema of the limbs, carried off the patient. The morbid appearances are very well described, " *In conspectum venit, uterque cordis ventriculus sanguine concreto repletus, et ultra modum distentus. Reperiuntur in sinistro carunculæ rotundæ substantiam pulmonis æmulantes ; quarum major ad avellanæ molem accedebat et aortæ ostium præcludebat.*"

I FIND among my notes, the history of a case of a disease of the heart, in some respects complicated. The girl was aged about eighteen, was of a slender make, and delicate constitution, and had never menstruated. About

four years before I saw her, she had accidentally
received a blow on the head, which had been
followed by symptoms of hydrocephalus. By
the application of repeated blisters to her head,
and the frequent use of submuriate of mercury, she got better, and continued tolerably
well for two years. At this time she complained of pain in the chest and lower part of the
abdomen; the action of the heart was jarring,
and its pulsation was more widely diffused than
usual; the pulse at the wrist, was irregular,
and frequently intermitting: her respiration
was laborious, and on using exertion, she was
threatened with suffocation; she frequently
awaked in a terror from some frightful dream,
and often she felt an indescribable anxiety in
the chest. As her disease advanced, the pulse
became smaller, weaker, and faultering, and
the pain in the pelvis was more acute. For
some months she had a tendency to syncope,
but never actually fainted till the month of November, 1804. After this, the faintness never
left her, the breathing became more and more laborious; the pulse became tremulous, and more
intermittent; the urine was passed in sparing
quantity, fluctuation was left in the abdomen,
her face and feet were œdematous, and she was
incessantly harassed with a short cough, attended with the expectoration of puriform mucus.

DIGITALIS, submuriate of mercury and squills,
alternated with gin punch, increased the flow

of urine, and in the course of two weeks, the most prominent symptoms were removed : from that time till the 20th of March, 1805, her health was better than it had been for some months before; but notwithstanding this, she was far from being well, her countenance was inflated, and she was unable to do more than move about the house, at a very slow pace.

ON the 21st of this month, she was suddenly, and without any obvious cause, seized with shivering and syncope, and for a long time, she continued very languid. When she was lying in this depressed state, her mother gave her about half a wine glassful of brandy, but it only for a short time revived her. When I now saw her, she was very low, and much oppressed; the pulse was hardly perceptible, yet her face was suffused; the breathing was extremely difficult, she had great anxiety in the chest, and pain beneath the sternum; the limbs were collapsed and cold.

SHE was directed to take small quantities occasionally of wine negus, rendered grateful by the addition of a little nutmeg; and she was advised to take, when she felt inclined, a few spoonfuls of calf-foot jelly, or any other light nourishment. She continued weak and languid for a few days, when she was attacked with diarrhœa, for which a grain of opium was prescribed, twice daily.

THE wine in a few days disagreed with her

stomach, and it was therefore laid aside; it was now found on examination, that the liver was enlarged, Dr. Baird recommended friction, with mercurial ointment over the right hypochondrium, and a blister was applied over the pained part of the chest.

IN two days, her mouth became affected, and the pulse rather increased in strength, but she had frequent returns of vomiting, excited by the cough, and without much change, she suddenly expired about the end of the month.

THE abdomen and thorax contained a quantity of serous fluid; the liver was slightly enlarged, but all the other abdominal contents were perfectly healthy. The lungs were also sound, and free from adhesion to the pleura costalis, except near to the spine on the left side, where they adhered firmly to the ribs; they were more solid than usual, and contained one or two small miciæ.

THE pericardium had within it, four ounces of an aqueous fluid; the right side of the heart was dilated, especially the auricle, which was covered with the lymphatic flaky crust, which is found in chronic inflammation; the substance of the aorta and coronary arteries, was perfectly healthy, but all the valves were in a diseased state; they were not actually ossified, but semi-cartilaginous, and the corpuscula Aurantii on the aortic valves, were indurated, and as thick as a split pea.

THIS girl had evidently from the first, a complicated disease. In the early stage, there is reason to believe, that the complaint was seated in the head, and also, that it was produced by the blow which she had r ceived there. From this history, a fact, which is by no means of unfrequent occurrence will be learned; I mean the subsequent affection of the liver and heart, after a complaint in the head. When she was again taken ill, at the distance of two years after the removal of the hydrocephalic symptoms, I would be inclined to think, from the pain in the pelvis, the jarring of the heart, and the diffusion of its pulsation; together with the irregularity of the pulse, and the œdema of her face, and other symptoms, that the morbid phenomena were produced, chiefly, if not altogether, by the chronic inflammation of the right auricle, and dropsy of the pericardium. This conjecture is, to my apprehension, strengthened by the beneficial effects of the digitalis, squills and calomel. The gin punch we would not have employed, had we not been misled by the pain in the pelvis, into the belief that the symptoms were in some measure connected with the suppression of the menstrual discharge. Probably it was about this time, that the valves began to suffer; and now, if you bear in recollection the progression of the symptoms, you will see that they correspond with the morbid phenomena, which were discovered by dissection. Also, the case shews how nearly such a state of the valves, produces effects resembling ossification of the coronary arteries.

IN this girl, had there not been actual difficulty in breathing, it would have been almost impossible *a priori* to have given any probable opinion as to the nature of the disease. If the complaint in its symptoms, had a resemblance to Syncope Anginosa, its termination was equally similar. You must have been struck with the resemblance between this case, and that of Mr. M. detailed by Dr. Parry, and I cannot but remark, that in both, stimuli were highly injurious. I have freely criticised the treatment of some of the cases of other practitioners, and it is but just, that I should confess where I have erred in my own plan of treatment. It has already, by several very eminent authors, been remarked, that if every practitioner were to detail his unsuccessful cases, equally freely as he does his successful, that we would be better able to judge of the real effects of remedies. In many cases, the fatal issue is laid to the charge of the disease, when in reality it has been accelerated by the remedies employed.

WHERE the obstruction to the passage of the blood is very complete, it has been known, that the parietes of the heart have given way during the contraction of its fibres. The heart bursts in precisely the same way, and for the same reason, that the uterus sometimes ruptures at the

instant that it expels the fœtus.   In a delicate
and slender young lady, who had for a length
of time, been subject to severe pain and constriction in the chest; with difficulty of breathing on climbing a hill, or running up stairs.
Mr. Russel conjectured from the symptoms
immediately preceding her death, that the heart
had given way.   This is, however, only supposition, for we were not permitted to examine
the body, and therefore we cannot be absolutely
certain, either that the previous thoracic complaints were produced by disease in the valves;
or that the immediate symptoms which carried
her off, were brought on by rupture of the heart.
By comparing, however, the symptoms in this
case, with those which had taken place in similar cases where the body was inspected, we are
almost authorised to conclude, that they were
brought on in all the instances by precisely the
same causes.

IN the case of this lady, the symptoms were
in some respects analogous to those accompanying Syncope Anginosa, in its incipient
stage; but we have no reason to believe, that
it really was a case of this disease.   The presence of dyspnœa and palpitation, are sufficient to attest that it was not.   The patient, as
I have mentioned, was always slender and delicate, but she was married, and had a child two
years old.   Along with her pectoral complaints,
she had been subject to very violent hysteric

paroxysms, which had hitherto been found more alarming than dangerous. Her friends were therefore not so much frightened as they would have been, had they never seen her in a hysteric fit before. She had, in the fatal attack, at the beginning, all the symptoms of a paroxysm of hysteria; she had difficulty in breathing, palpitation of the heart, flatulence, and convulsive agitation of the limbs, along with hysteric sobbing. By the use of proper remedies, the violence of the paroxysm was always abated, but a new one soon succeeded After she had for a few hours been better than usual, she was suddenly seized with a fit, more than usual violent. During this paroxysm, her face was suddenly blanched, and the features collapsed; she was bathed in a cold and clammy sweat; the extremities were cold; her pulse became exceedingly feeble and small, and it beat only once for every two contractions of the heart. There was also a great degree of oppression about the region of the heart; and there was a very unusual fluttering in the breast. Till her death, which happened in the course of a couple of days, she was every now and then attacked with fits of irregular muscular action and vomiting, and she died at last completely exhausted.

From these phenomena, it is probable, that during the action of the heart, some part of it had given way, owing to the obstruction to the passage of the blood from its cavities. Were it allowable to speculate on what had taken place, I would imagine, that the valves at the root of the aorta had, in this instance, been diseased, and that the left auricle or ventricle had given way. My reason for supposing that the aortic valves were those affected, arises from the great difficulty she experienced in breathing, or using fatiguing exercise; and we have reason to believe, from the length of time she survived, that only a very small rupture had taken place. The double stroke of the heart may perhaps be explained, by supposing, that as now the pericardium must have contained a quantity of blood, so must the heart have been compressed, and thus only a small quantity of blood would on each contraction of the ventricle, have been sent into the great artery; not such a quantity as would excite its contraction; this would require a new impulse of blood from the heart. We cannot, however, from the presence of the double stroke of the heart, infer that the heart had really burst. In many cases, for a great length of time, there is a want of correspondence between the action of the heart and the vessels. Indeed, it is generally noticed, in the descriptions of authors, that when the aortic valves are ossified, the pulse does not beat so frequently as the heart. When, however, we take this symptom into account, along with the sudden sinking of the strength,

and blanching and collapse of the countenance,
it is rendered probable, that this event had actually taken place. This supposition is further
corroborated by the observation of the celebrated Portal, who found in many cases of sudden death, that the heart had given way during its own action; and what might at first
sight appear strange, he has found that the left
side is more frequently burst than the right,
and the ventricle oftner than the auricle. In
Morgagni's letters, one or two cases will be
found related, in which the left ventricle had
given way. If we view the matter, however, in
its proper light, we can readily understand
how this happens. We see an analogous effect in the laceration of the strong fibres of the
gastrocnemius muscle, by its own powerful contraction. If we obstruct the passage of the
blood from the right ventricle into the pulmonary artery, we find, that we give that side of
the heart, and the veins near it, a tendency to
augment both their cavity and solid substance.
When the mitral valve is obstructed, we find
that the blood impelled by the pulmonary artery, meeting in its course, a back stroke from
the left auricle, produces rupture of the minute
branches of those vessels in the lungs.

SOME may here inquire, why this does not at
all times take place where the pulmonary circulation is obstructed? I reply, because, in proportion to the slowly increasing resistance to the

passage of the blood, the coats of the vessels are
equally augmenting their power; and, therefore,
we observe, that laceration of the vessels never
takes place, except where the circulation has
been hurried. To prove this, I might adduce the
evidence of a long list of authors, but I believe
that a sufficient number of examples have been
already brought forward. Let however the passage of the blood from the left ventricle into
the aorta be obstructed, while at the same time
the mitral valve is perfect, then accelerate the
circulation, and watch the effect. After the
acceleration has gone on to a certain extent, the
parietes of the ventricle will burst, as we have
reason to believe, happened by a very small
opening, in the lady attended by Mr. Russel.
Sometimes, however, a large rent is formed
in it, and in this case, death is very sudden.
In one case communicated by Chaussier to
Portal, the left auricle was burst, by a carriage
wheel passing over the arch of the aorta, and
in another case where the valves were rigid, the
dilated auricle burst. This, however, can only
happen, when the mitral valves act imperfectly: where they are healthy, the ventricle gives
way " la rupture des ventricules est ordináire-
" ment, comme on l'a dit precedemment, la
" suite du retrecissement de leurs orifices ar-
" terielles, occasionné par le gonflement de leur
" cercle ligamenteux, ou par l'ossification de
" leurs valvules."   " On a trouvé le ventricule

" droit et gauche ouverts dans la même sujet." If we had a full history of such a case, it would make a valuable addition, for probably we should find, that both the pulmonic and aortic valves were diseased; the latter, however, more than the former; and it is also likely, that we should be able to trace the history of the fatal attack to some sudden and violent exertion. In a rare case, I have been informed, that an indurated aortic valve, instead of causing rupture of the heart itself, burst, and was on the death of the person, found ruptured.

THE induration of the valves is, in some cases, not productive of quite so much obstruction to the blood as in others; and when this happens, the phenomena are somewhat modified. In a case which occurred, when Dr. Brown was in the Edinburgh hospital, and which, along with many other valuable manuscripts, he very obligingly allowed me to make use of, the patient had, in the first instance, all the symptoms of inflammation of the liver, complicated with dropsy. These by the use of proper remedies " seemed to be removed; but then " the symptoms of an affection of the heart " came on. There was a jarring when the ven- " tricles contracted; and when the hand was " laid on the side, it resembled the feel of a " varicose aneurism; his expectoration, when he " used exercise was bloody; he had unusual pal- " pitation, jarring sensation, and hissing noise,

" as of several currents meeting; the sound
" was frequently audible, as in the varicose
" aneurism; the pulse did not correspond with
" the action of the heart, it was feeble, yet the
" contraction of the artery was made with
" rapidity."

ON dissection, the mitral valve was found indurated, and reticulated, and the right auricle
was enlarged; the liver and lungs were hardened, and the pericardium was inflamed.

THIS case, the history of which I did not receive, till after I had nearly finished my manu-
script, illustrates some circumstances which have
been shewn to accompany partial obstruction
of the passage of the blood through the lungs.
Enlargement of the right side of the heart,
induration of the mitral valves, and rigidity of
the valves in the mouth of the aorta, are each
of them under certain circumstances, productive of bloody expectoration. Dr. Rutherford,
in his Clinical Observations on this case, remarks; that from the reticulation of the valve,
" there seemed to be an opening left between
" the auricle and ventricle, during the contrac-
" tion of the latter. Thus on each contraction,
" the blood flowed in part into the aorta, in
" part into the left auricle, producing regurgita-
" tion along the pulmonary veins, and obstruc-
" tion to this circulation." In this way, it will
be seen, that although the blood be not nearly so
much impeded in its passage from the auricle into

the ventricle, as in the other cases already described; that yet, from the state of the mitral valve permitting regurgitation into the auricle, the same effects are really produced on the pulmonary vessels; and it must strike you, that in a case of this kind, on hurrying the circulation by exercise, by hard drinking, or by anger, the same effects will follow, as result from the application of the same exciting causes, in a person in whom the right side of the heart is dilated. The regurgitation of the blood from the ventricle into the auricle, must have produced both the jarring sensation, and also, as Dr. Rutherford notices, the hissing noise as of several currents meeting. In all probability, it is something of this kind which is described as audible palpitation, in some diseases of the heart.

WHEN the arterial valves are thickened and corrugated, and incapable of covering the orifice which they ought to guard, we find that the symptoms are generally pretty nearly the same with those mentioned in the last case, but in other instances they are not very prominently marked; nay, in some cases, the person dies without any suspicion of being affected with any serious disease. A girl, while employed one morning in the laborious occupation of washing heavy clothes, was seized with a sudden fit of illness; she had just time to turn to her companion, when she fell down dead, by the side of her tub. The aorta was thickened and indurated, and the semi-lunar valves were rigid and imperfect; each flap was at least the eighth part of an inch thick; all of them were corrugated, and one was so puckered, as not to be larger than a split pea. In this girl, the valves were in such a state, that they were incompetent to close the passage from the ventricle into the aorta. They were so much diseased, that they would prevent the free transmission of the blood from the heart into the artery, but at the same time, their condition was such, that they would have less influence in this way, than in allowing a part of the blood on the contraction of the vessel to return into the ventricle.

FROM these two causes, there must have been a deficiency of arterial blood in the vascular system. The patient must have had an incapacity to exert herself, as she had been wont to do ; but in her, as the disease was on the increase, the circulation was while tranquil, carried on tolerably well. When however she over-exerted herself, as she did the morning before her death, the effects of the altered state of the aortic' valves, would come to be more seriously felt. From the repercussions of the aorta being now frequent, blood must very often have been driven back into the ventricle. It must have gained on that cavity, producing an irregularity in the action of the heart, which would soon induce a state of deep syncope. Here I would observe, that death is at first, probably only apparent, and I would wish to impress on your minds, an idea, that by due perseverance in the means of resuscitation, life may in some instances be restored. And I would also wish you to understand, that by procrastination in employing these means, the apparent death is in a time, which, *a priori*, cannot be specified, exchanged for real death. If therefore, you are to make any attempt to restore animation, you will do well to commence your operations as soon as you can reach the place where the patient is laid; and here, as in every case of asphyxia, you will probably be obliged to persist in the use of the necessary means, for a considerable length of time, before you can be certain of either succeeding or failing. In regard to the plan of palliation, little can be added to what has already been said, when treating of Syncope Anginosa, for what applies to the one, is equally applicable to the other.

OBSERVATIONS

ON THE FORMATION OF POLYPI IN THE HEART.

THAT polypus of the heart ever exists as an idiopathic affection, is far from being proved; but no doubt can reasonably be entertained, respecting the formation of these morbid productions, in some diseases of this organ. Among the ancient practitioners, much importance was attached to the lymphatic clots which were often found in the heart; but although these are now incontrovertibly proved, to be a general consequence of death; and although our ancestors have often, like too many of the moderns, indulged in idle speculations, are we thencé authorised to deny altogether, that real polypi ever exist in the heart? To think so, would be absurd; it is sufficient that we destroy the ideal consequence, which was formerly attached to the current histories of polypi, and of cells in the heart, and that we shew, that in few or none of these cases, was the concretion really a part of the disease. If we strictly scrutinize all the reputed cases of polypus in the heart, we shall reduce the real examples of this affection to a very limited number indeed. Still we shall leave a few, where there is reason to believe that the concretion had been formed a very considerable time before death; but it must be understood, that these concretions are seldom found, except in hearts otherwise diseased. In health, the blood does not tarry for any length of time in either the heart or vessels; it is incessantly in motion, circulating with greater or less rapidity, according to the state of the heart and arteries. The blood never in health remains so long in contact with the surfaces of the heart, as to allow of its being changed by their action. In some diseases of this organ, irregular actions are excited by very trifling causes; the blood stagnates longer in the heart than it usually does, or ought to do, while here it undergoes changes by the reciprocal action of the blood on the heart, and of the heart, on the blood; new organised matter is deposited, and adheres to the parietes of the cavity in which it is lodged. This concretion slowly increases, the first particle acting as the exciting cause for the deposition of the second, and so on. While it is progressively on the increase, it is insidiously adding to the danger of the primary disease. It exasperates the general symptoms, but is seldom productive of any single symptom so well defined, as to be considered characteristic of the affection. Mr. John Bell, who is very much inclined to doubt the existence of polypi in the heart, views the case of Mr. Holder, as the one which bears the nearest resemblance to this complaint of any on record. I have examined this case, and instead of being a case of polypus, it appears to me, nothing more than a description of the usual consequences, resulting from imperfect action of the valves. The noise, as of the rushing of water, is to me a proof that the case was nearly similar to that treated by Dr. Rutherford, and we have here reason to believe, that the concretion was as in most cases, only symptomatic of a more serious affection of the heart.

IN diseases of the heart, attended with impaired action of this organ, we cannot doubt, but that these concretions were formed at a period considerably antecedent to death. In one case dissected by Dr. Monro, Sen. the parietes of the ventricle at the spot where the polypus was attached, were found membranous. In a few instances which have come under our own review, we have found these new productions composed of different layers of cream coloured firm substance, without a single red globule entering into their composition, although they were immersed am ng uid blood, and surrounded with sanguineous coagula. In two of our cases, a membranous looking capsule incircled the polypus, which was composed of firm concentric layers; which facts surely seem to favour the opinion, that in these instances the polypi were possessed of a preservative as well as a formative power. The roots of these productions, in the cases to which I allude, were interwoven among the musculi pectinati; and at the point where they were fixed to the heart, the inner surface of the auricle was rough, and its investing membrane seemed wanting. Most of the coagula which are found in the cardiac cavities, are indisputably formed *in articulo mortis,* but I think the following history will shew, that this is not always the case.

" ROBERT MAITLAND, was admitted a pa-
" tient into the Glasgow Royal Infirmary, on

" the 4th of May, 1806. He said that a year be-
" fore, he had been affected with hœmoptysis,
" which, since that period, had recurred several
" times. He had been free from it for four
" months past, and knew no cause that had
" originally brought it on. He had used various
" medicines without any relief. He was troubled
" at his admission with a short hard cough,
" attended with a thick purulent expectoration,
" free from any admixture of blood. He felt at
" times a sense of oppression and anxiety at the
" upper and fore part of the thorax, but was
" free from dyspnœa; his appetite was good,
" and his thirst natural; he was subject to oc-
" casional rigours during the day, and to pro-
" fuse sweats at night. Pulse 92, rather irregu-
" lar, belly natural. Two blisters were applied
" in succession to the breast, and he began the
" use of tincture of digitalis, which he continu-
" ed till the 12th of June, when the symptoms
" being considerably mitigated, he was dismis-
" sed at his own desire. In the course of three
" days, he presented himself for re-admission,
" saying that he was troubled with dyspnœa,
" that the cough continued, and that the ex-
" pectoration was now streaked with blood. He
" again began the use of the tincture of digita-
" lis, and became rather easier, till the 21st,
" when he complained for the first time of pain
" in the left side of the thorax; a blister was
" applied to the affected part, but with little

" effect. On the 11th of July, after taking
" more exercise than usual, he was affected
" with a sense of oppression at the heart, and
" expectorated a considerable quantity of florid
" spumous blood. The purulent expectoration
" became mixed with a greater quantity of
" blood than ever, and the cough continued as
" before; on the 13th, after much coughing, he
" expectorated at least ℔j of florid blood, was
" affected with most distressing dyspnœa, and
" was incapable of remaining in any posture,
" except the semi-erect: pulse 130, he had a
" blister applied to the breast, and he was direct-
" ed to use the nitrous mixture. On the 14th
" he felt considerably relieved; and the report
" of the 15th states, that there is no appearance
" of blood in the sputum, and the respiration is
" more free. 16th, Early this morning, began
" to spit up such quantity of blood, that he ap-
" peared threatened with immediate suffocation;
" pulse very irregular and weak. About two
" o'clock in the afternoon, the pulse was 120,
" and rather full, and he complained of much
" difficulty of breathing. He was ordered to be
" bled, but the pulse having fallen consider-
" ably within an hour, the bleeding was delay-
" ed. At eleven o'clock, as he complained of
" considerable oppression in the breast, and his
" pulse was frequent and full, six ounces of
" blood were drawn from his arm; after the
" bleeding, he felt relieved, but very feeble; he

" was however sensible, and remained so till
" early on the 17th, when he expired at eight
" o'clock in the morning."

THIS is the history of the case, which, along
with the heart, I had from Mr. de Lys, at that
time house surgeon to the hospital. From the
symptoms we might *a priori* have been led to
expect, that on dissection the right side of the
heart would have been found dilated; but I do
not know that there were any certain signs, by
which we could prognosticate the existence
of a polypus concretion in the heart. When
the body was examined, the right auricle and
ventricle were found considerably dilated; and
in the former, a large and fully organised polypus was lodged; its attachment was by a rough
surface to the *musculi pectinati*, and its body
hung down into the right ventricle. It very
much, in appearance, resembled a nasal polypus, and it was so firmly fixed to the heart,
that it allowed the whole mass of the heart, and
a considerable portion of the lungs, to be suspended by it, without shewing any tendency
to separate. It was pendulous, and tapered
from below upward; its structure was dense,
lammellated, and not a single red globule entered into its composition.

IN reviewing the detail of symptoms, we find
it stated, that three days after the man was pro-
nounced cured, the symptoms recurred ; now,
it is very much to be regretted, that no particu-

lar enquiry was made as to the cause of the renewal of the bleeding from the lungs. Had proper investigation been made, it is more than
probable, that as he had just left the house, and
got home among his friends, he had indulged in
spirituous liquors; or that in his eagerness to
visit them, he had fatigued himself: at this time
the dilatation of the right side must have been
considerable, and perhaps during some of the irregularities of its action, the polypus had begun
to form : These two morbid conditions, would naturally aid each other in the induction of deranged action. He is next reported to have expectorated fluid, tinged with blood ; this is easily accounted for, when we recollect what takes place
in accelerating the action of a heart, where the
right side is larger than the left. This attack,
left the heart in a ticklish condition; its function unequal, its power diminished, and so extremely apt to suffer from slight causes, that
you see it is reported, on the 13th of July, that
by unusual exertion, the accommodation of the
quantity of blood sent out by the right side of
the heart, to the capacity of the left, was again
destroyed; instead of an expectoration, which
before, had merely been streaked with blood,
there was now a profuse discharge of florid blood
from the lungs; there was an entensive læsion of
the bronchial vessels; and here I would take occasion to observe, that the bright colour of the
blood is no proof that it did not come from the

right side. It is true, indeed, that when the blood is projected from the right ventricle, it is dark in complexion, in composition venous, but these properties are exchanged for others in the course of circulation through the lungs; hence as long as the air is admitted in any tolerable quantity, whenever either the ultimate branches of the pulmonary artery, or the commencement of the pulmonary veins give way, the blood coughed up is both florid and frothy. After this, till the 14th, he continued to labour under distressing dyspnœa, a symptom referable to the retention and coagulation of a portion of the blood in the bronchial cells. The further effusion of blood would now seem to have ceased, and it is even probable, that a considerable portion of the coagulum pressing on the air cells, had been removed by absorption; for it is reported, that he was much relieved in the course of two days.

BUT, by these attacks, the action of the heart was irreparably injured; consequently, on the 16th he had a violent paroxysm of hæmoptysis, the effusion was so great as to threaten suf-focation, and in the end did prove fatal; an event assuredly accelerated by venesection, pre-scribed and employed during an interval, when the pulse was fuller than usual. An intelligent practitioner would never have been misled by a feeling of this kind, for he would naturally have been suspicious of its being counterfeited, in place of real strength. If stimuli in such cases deserve to be reprobated, the untimely use of the lancet ought to be as severely censured.

To these proofs of the vitality of some polypi, I may add another deduced from the diseased state in which we found the polypus itself, in a person who had evidently died from Angina Pectoris. In this subject, the nutrient arteries of the heart were extensively ossified; the aortic valves had fungi attached to their floating margins, and one of the chordæ tendineæ was implanted in such a way into one of the semi-lunar valves, as to destroy in a great measure its valvular action. In the left ventricle, a polypus concretion which measured more than one inch in length, was found attached to the septum of the heart. That side of the polypus next to the septum, adhered so firmly to it, that the membrane lining the ventricle tore, before the polypus could be separated from the heart. Where the two were in contact, the septum was painted with small red vessels, and was besides rough. This fact of the firm union of the polypus with the heart, is a sufficient proof of the vitality of the latter; but this is established beyond a doubt, by an abscess being found in the centre of the polypus itself. This abscess, when opened, discharged above a tea spoonful of perfectly formed purulent matter.

In this dissection, I would particularly call your attention to the existence of the polypus, and the diseased nutrient arteries. Can we have a more unexceptionable proof than this dissection affords of the causes which predispose to the formation of polypi; and is it possible to procure a more satisfactory argument in favour of the vitality of some polypi, than the one furnished by this subject? The ossification of the coronary arteries, and their otherwise diseased state clearly shew, that the action of this heart must have been languid; and the presence of a fully organised polypus, corroborates a position formerly laid down: It tends to establish the point, that impaired action of the heart predisposes to the formation of polypi. The existence of the abscess in the centre of the polypus, surely shews that the concretion had been endowed with vitality: It also, I think, proves that the polypus must have existed a considerable time before death.

THE polypi we have been just describing, are, without doubt, merely formed from the blood changed by the action of the vessels of the heart, and supported by twigs from the coronary vessels; but there is another species of concretion occasionally met with in the heart, where the cavity in which it is contained, is much more extensively affected. In this disease, the parietes of the heart are generally thickened, in spots ossified, and the inner surface of the cavity is rugged, and lined with the same kind of substance which invests the inside of aneurismal tumors. This species of concretion has very much the look of being a fungus from the heart itself, and is altogether unlike the other polypi, which seem productions in the first instance from the blood contained in the cavities of the heart. We have in our possession, a heart where the concretion is as large as a pullet's egg, and where it is attached by a broad base to the side of the left auricle, which, over its whole extent, is thickened and diseased; and in this instance, by forcing air into the coronary vein, we could inflate some few vessels in the new formed substance, in which there were likewise some specks of bone. In this person, the mitral valve was so malformed, that the presence of the polypus in the auricle, was a matter of complete indifference. Indeed, as has already been noticed, we have great reason to doubt, whether a case of idiopathic polypus of the heart has ever occurred. If blended with other diseases, its presence can rarely before death be ascertained; and if discovered, it would not alter the plan of treatment.

ANEURISM OF THE THORACIC AORTA.

ANEURISM of the thoracic aorta, is so inti-
mately connected with the diseases of the heart,
that it is often mistaken for a cardiac affection.
This renders it necessary for me to notice this disease, but I do not in this place propose to enter
on the consideration of the doctrines of aneurism in general. Scarpa, the accurate and indefatigable Italian anatomist, has collected such
a number of facts relating to the pathology of
this disease, that he has left very little to be
done by any succeeding writer on this part of
the subject. This author, by cautious induction from his own dissections, and from the la-
bours of others in the same field, has been led to
adopt the opinion of a rupture of the internal
coats of the artery, being an invariable precur-
sor of real aneurism.

FROM this view of the subject, Professor
Scarpa observes, " That the root of an aneu-
" rism of the aorta, in whatever point of this
" artery it appears, never includes the whole
" circumference of the tube of the artery ; but
" that the root constantly occupies and in-
" volves only the one or the other side of the
" artery, from which side, the aneurismal sac

" rises and enlarges in the form of an appen-
" dix or tuberosity." Whoever has had any
opportunity of dissecting aortic aneurisms, and
has carefully compared the morbid phenomena
which he has observed with the description of
the Italian Professor, must acknowledge the
fidelity and accuracy of the general detail.
Perhaps, however, it may not be uniformly
found, that " the root of an aneurism never in-
" cludes the whole circumference of the tube
" of the artery." We have a preparation in
which the reverse has taken place. In this case,
the whole cylinder of the vessel, from the heart
to beyond the curvature, is equally dilated; and
dilated to such an extent, that the tumor measures no less than ten inches in circumference.

THIS case, I mention, not that it may be
put in opposition to the observations of Scarpa,
which are founded on too wide a basis, to be
affected by any isolated and anomalous variety
of diseased structure; but I mention it, to shew
that there are instances, though very rare, in
which the artery is really enlarged and diseased
in its whole circumference. Professor Scarpa
is ready to allow, that in dilatation, the canal
of the artery is equally affected all round, but
he considers this as a very different disease
from aneurism. He says, " there is really a re-
" markable difference between a dilated artery,
" and an aneurismatic artery, although these
" two affections are sometimes found combined

" together, especially at the beginning of the
" aorta, as it comes out of the heart. Further,
" if we consider in general, that the dilatation
" of an artery may exist without any affection,
" properly speaking organic, the blood being
" always contained within its cavity; that in
" the tract of the artery, somewhat increased in
" diameter, there are never formed nor collect-
" ed any grumous blood or polypous layers; that
" the dilatation of the diameter of an artery,
" never becomes of such a size, as to form a
" tumor of considerable bulk; and lastly, that as
" long as the continuity of the proper coats of
" the artery remains uninterrupted, the circu-
" lation of the blood is not at all, or not so sen-
" sibly changed; then we shall be obliged to al-
" low, that aneurism differs essentially from the
" dilatation of an artery."

FROM this quotation, it will appear, that
Scarpa limits dilatation to that state of an artery, in which the coats remain in their natural relation to each other, and in which they
are not altered in their texture, nor lined on
their inner surface with " polypous layers."
This, however, was not the case in the instance
which I have brought forward. In it you have
seen that the coats were much dilated, and
also very much altered in their structure. Externally and internally, they had assumed the
look of the membranes of the fœtus, only they
were thicker and denser, but they were equal-

ly gelatinous, and nearly as tranparent; and on their inner surface, they were crusted over with laminæ of coagulating lymph. By peeling off this incrustation, after the sac had been inverted, we saw plainly, that although the internal coats were round the complete cylinder of the vessel much diseased, and considerably dilated, yet they were not dilated to the same degree as the external coverings of the artery; at irregular distances, longitudinal rents were formed in the fibrous coats, and these chasms were filled with coagulating lymph. The internal coats over the whole circumference of the vessel had assumed the diseased condition, which in aneurism, is generally confined to a part of the cylinder. From this circumstance, therefore, the whole circumference of the artery came to be dilated, but still the outer coverings were those which were chiefly enlarged.

IN these respects, you will at once perceive, that the disease bore the character of genuine aneurism, except in regard to the uniform dilatation of the whole circumference of the artery. In this tumor, all the coats continued for a time to dilate equally, but at length the internal gave way, forming longitudinal rents through which the external coats could be seen, after the lymphatic coating had been scraped off. In this instance, had the sac been dissected in the early stage, it would have presented precisely the same appearance as those described by Dr.

Monro, and the one lately examined by the Surgical Editor of the London Medical Review, who is well known for his accurate and extensive anatomical knowledge.

AFTER all that has been said and written on the Anatomy of Aneurism, I think it may fairly be questioned, if ever the sac has, or can acquire a large size, without rupture of the inner coats of the artery. The tumor described by the Editor of the London Medical Review, is the largest I believe, on record, in which all the coats have been found uniformly dilated. From attending to what has taken place in other instances, it is reasonable to infer, that had this person lived longer, and had the sac continued to increase in size, the inner coats of the artery would have burst. This supposition becomes probable, when we contemplate the state in which the internal coat of the vessel was found: " the sac, which would contain the fist of a mid-" dle sized man, is lined throughout with flakes " of bone, and though the internal coat of the " vessel which is thus patched, is extremely thin " and brittle, it does not on minute inspection " any where exhibit a solution of continuity." Had the cyst, however, by an increased impetus of the blood from the heart been preternaturally distended, the fragile internal coat would probably have ruptured, while the more elastic external covering might have continued for a time entire.

HAVING made these remarks, it is but just to inform you, that the case I have just related, is the only one out of fourteen, we have dissected, which did not corroborate in every point the observations of the Italian Anatomist. Although Morgagni states, that in aneurism of the aorta, the vessel is sometimes uniformly enlarged, he yet expressly observes, that this is a rare occurrence. The result of his experience is therefore decidedly in support of Scarpa's doctrine.

HILDANUS, in the 17th century, made an approach toward a just theory of the pathology of aneurism; but his successor Sennertus, is more clear and explicit on this subject, for he taught, that in aneurism, whether external or internal, the innermost coats of the artery are ruptured, the external alone dilated. He is therefore to be considered as the parent of our pathology of this disease. This theory was opposed by Muraltus and Freind, the latter of whom, supposed that the external coat, from its laxness, must of necessity be ruptured by the same cause which burst the internal tunics; but the former admitted, that the internal coats might be ruptured, without a laceration of the external coverings of the artery, in those cases where they, during the ulceration of the former, had their strength preternaturally increased. The Italian Professor is a keen advocate for the theory of Sennertus, which, in many respects, is analogous to the one which he adopts. In its leading features, it bears a correct resemblance to it, but it is deficient in some of the subordinate details. Professor Scarpa, has most indisputably rendered it certain, that in all the cases which he had seen of aneurism, there had been a rupture of the internal coats of the vessel; and in all the cases recorded in practical works which have come under his view, and he has been most industrious in collecting facts, he has demonstrated, that where proper attention has been bestowed on the dissection, it has generally been mentioned, that appearances were seen which can only be explained on the supposition of a rupture of the internal coats of the artery. We have therefore every reason to believe, that in the majority of cases of aneurism of the aorta, the internal coats are lacerated, the external alone dilated.

SCARPA, after tracing very accurately the relation which the cellular coat bears to the deep seated coats, and also to the parts externally in its vicinity; and after having pointed out the consequences of rupturing the internal coats, and then forcing air into the vessel, adds, " The phe-
" nomena which are observable in the artificial
" distensions of the thoracic or abdominal aorta,
" present themselves likewise, in my opinion, in
" the case of a morbid degeneration of the in-
" ternal coat of the artery; during which, that
" coat becomes in some places weak, or very
" rigid and pliable; and is thinned, separated

" or ruptured by the repeated jets of blood
" thrown from the heart. The internal coat of
" an artery being ulcerated or lacerated from a
" slow internal cause in some point of its cir-
" cumference, the blood impelled by the heart,
" begins immediately to ooze through the con-
" nections of the fibres of the muscular coat,
" and gradually to be effused into the interstices
" of the cellular covering, which supplies the
" place of a sheath to the injured artery, and
" forms for a certain space, a kind of ecchy-
" mosis or extravasation of blood, slightly ele-
" vated upon the artery ; afterwards, the points
" of contact between the edges of the fibres of
" the muscular coat being insensibly separated,
" the arterial blood penetrating between, fills
" and elevates in a remarkable manner the
" cellular covering of the artery, and raises it
" after the manner of an incipient tumor.
" Thus, the fibres and layers of the muscular
" coat, being wasted or lacerated or simply se-
" parated from each other, the arterial blood is
" carried with greater force, and in greater
" quantity than before into the cellular sheath
" of the artery, which it forces more outwards ;
" and finally, the divisions between the inter-
" stices of the cellular coat being ruptured,
" converts it into a sac which is filled with po-
" lypous concretions, and with fluid blood, and
" at last, forms, properly speaking, the aneuris-
" mal sac, the internal texture of which, al-

" though apparently composed of membranous
" plicæ, placed one over the other, is in fact
" very different from that of the proper coats
" of the artery; notwithstanding the injured
" artery both in the thorax and in the abdomen,
" as well as the aneurismal sac, is covered ex-
" ternally, and inclosed within a common smooth
" membrane."

From this quotation it is clear, that Scarpa
believes, that in the early stage of aneurism,
the cellular coat of the vessel is possessed of
its healthy texture; and he even speaks of the
blood distending its cells. He attempts to illustrate the succession of phenomena, by ex-
periments made on dead vessels; but on the
result of these, we can place very little depen-
dance. Even however, if we incline to give
them full weight, we find that they rather mili-
tate against the doctrine of aneurism, being dependent on the forcing of the blood among the
cells of the external covering of the artery.
Take an artery, whose internal coats are diseased, ossified, or cartilaginous, for example, and
whose external covering is healthy, and inject
wax into it, and observe what happens; you
will see that at first the injection is confined to
the proper canal of the vessel, but that by distending this, the internal coats rupture, when
immediately the wax penetrates between the
cellular coat and the one next it, separating the
one from the other to a great extent. The wax
is never collected in a circumscribed cyst, as

the blood is in aneurism; on the contrary, it is diffused over a great extent of the artery, and it even compresses the internal coats, puckering them sometimes so much, as almost to obliterate the canal of the vessel: In aneurism, we never find this diffusion of the blood.

ALTHOUGH therefore, it be certainly true, that in aneurism, the cellular coat of the vessel is generally alone dilated, yet it is a mistake to suppose, that in this disease, this coat is in its natural state: on the contrary, even in the incipient stage of the complaint, not only the cellular coat of the artery is much changed, but likewise the pericardium investing it is generally altered in its appearance; both of them are thicker and firmer than in health, and there is also in many cases, a new effusion between them. They are in fact, not to be recognised as the original coverings of the artery, except by their position. They are no more like the natural cellular coat and pericardium, than a tendon is like a muscle. They are in every respect, new formed parts, though they occupy the place of the former coats of the artery; and we have in our dissections, uniformly found the inner surface of the cellular coat crusted over with lymphatic glazing, and that, whether the tumor was large or small. If the cellular coat of the vessel, at the time that the rupture of the internal tunics of the artery takes place, be not thickened and rendered firmer than usual, it would be incapable of retaining the blood. Indeed, I have in one case, where the tumor was seated at the root of the aorta, and where it was not bigger than a hazel nut, been able clearly to demonstrate, not only the uncommon solidity of the cellular coat, but also I was able to shew that the limits of the sac were defined by a preternaturally firm adhesion of the outer to the inner coats round the root of the cyst. Had this adhesion of the outer to the inner coats not taken place, how could the tumor have been raised from the side of the vessel like a large wart from the finger; would not the blood, had this attachment been wanting, have forced its way along the tract of the vessel, detaching the coats from each other to an unbounded extent, as we see happen in our injections after death.

CAN we, seeing these facts, allow ourselves even for a moment to believe, that if the internal fibrous coats of a healthy vessel be burst, the lax cellular coat shall be able to confine the blood, forming at the instant that the aneurism begins, a tumor small as a bean, and beating with furious pulsation. We cannot give credit to it, but we can readily comprehend as Muraltus observes, how, when an artery has lost its contractile power, and has by a slow alteration had its cellular coat rendered thicker, firmer, and fixed by preternatural adhesion to the internal coats beyond the diseased spot, the blood may, when the internal coats rupture, be confined by the diseased external covering. We can, if this previous change be admitted, understand the theory of Sennertus, and follow the accurate and convincing reasoning of Scarpa. I do not however, pretend to say, that in every case of aortic aneurism, the pericardiac or pleuretic covering is diseased, I only wish to be understood, as representing this to be a frequent occurrence. I have seen cases in which these were healthy, and in which they were joined to the diseased cellular coat by healthy cellular membrane. I have been induced to make these observations on Professor Scarpa's work, from observing what had taken place in several instances of aneurism, which I have had an opportunity of dissecting; yet it will be perceived, that the points in which I have ventured to differ from this author, are those which have been commented on by others, and more especially by Muraltus. On the other parts of the theory and practice in aneurism, Scarpa has left little room for criticism; his facts are well established, and his deductions are fair inferences from his data.

IT is at first sight astonishing, that from the year 1557, when Vesalius first discovered aneurism of the aorta, so little progress should have been made in the history of this disease. From that period to the present, a number of books have been published on aneurism, some of the authors taking a wider, others a more limited view of their subject; Scarpa has certainly the merit of being the first, who has made a judicious selection of the scattered facts belonging to the history of this disease, and who has arranged them in such a way, as to produce a connected account of this most dangerous complaint.

ANEURISM of the thoracic aorta, is more frequent perhaps, than that of any other vessel in the body. I have had an opportunity of examining fourteen, who had died of this complaint, but have not seen more than three instances of external aneurism. In aneurism of the aorta, we can often trace the commencement of the disease to some violent exertion on the part of the patient, but at other times, it begins without any obvious cause. The fibrous coats of the artery, lose their natural structure; they are slowly changed either into a cartilaginous, bony, or steatomatus looking matter: They cease to be able to re-act on the blood; they have now neither elasticity nor muscular power, therefore by the *vis a tergo*, they burst at the weakest point. The blood now insinuates itself between the external and the internal coats; it detaches the former from its connection with the latter, as far as the disease of the internal coats extends; beyond this, it cannot separate them, the adhesion there having become preternaturally firm. The rupture of the internal coats of an artery, is not the first part of the process which takes place in the production of an aneurism.

Before this happens, we find, that the external coat has, all round the diseased part of the proper coats of the vessel, been fixed to the healthy coats more firmly than usual ; and also, that the texture of the cellular coat, has suffered a change, for now it is denser and thicker than natural. These changes precede the bursting of the fibrous coats. When the internal coats have given way, the external, being unable to resist the impulse of the blood, distend; a tumor forms on the side of the vessel, attached often by a very narrow neck to the artery, but expanding afterwards into a diffused globular or pyriform swelling.

THIS tumor is at first small and hard, as we see on dissecting those who have died in the incipient stage of the disease, and if there be any analogy between the symptoms of external and internal aneurism, the tumor will be raised and depressed alternately by the *vis a tergo*. In proportion as the disease advances, the tumor for a time becomes softer and larger, but at last it becomes pretty solid, for as it is placed off from the direct course of the circulation, and as its coverings have no power of contraction, the blood stagnates in its cavity, where it in part coagulates. These lymphatic coagula augment the thickness of the sides of the sac, but they hardly increase their strength, they are not themselves possessed of any great share of vitality, therefore, in proportion as the cyst dilates, they rupture at different points: Hence, when we open an aneurismal tumor, we find it from this cause, ragged and unequal on its inner surface ; and we can even trace the successive rents, which have taken place in its lymphatic lining.

WHERE the disease does not at this time prove fatal, we find that the tumor occasionally becomes of a monstrous size. As it enlarges, it presses on the ribs, the sternum, or whatever bone it may happen to be in contact with ; its constant and slowly increasing pressure on these, produces absorption of their earthy parts. The chest is burst open, the tumor then appears externally, attaining afterwards in some cases, to the almost incredible size of a full grown person's head. When this conversion of the complaint from internal to external aneurism takes place, the fate of the patient is for the most part soon decided. The sac, from its nature, is very apt to fall into a state of slow inflammatory action. This process, when it has once begun, gradually proceeds, the neighbouring parts are made to assume the same condition; the huge pulsating mass is soon covered by thin and livid integuments, which have assumed such a degree of transparency as to shew their vessels enlarged; and from the mixture of the arteries and veins, but preponderance of the latter, the colour of the skin is purple inclining to red. As the tumor enlarges, the coverings of the sac gradually become thinner; and at last, when they are almost as thin as paper, the most prominent point of the skin becomes fretted. This excoriation assumes a phagedenic appearance, and penetrates deeper, till at length on the separation of a small slough, the blood begins to escape. At first however, the stream is not continued, the hæmorrhage is for a short time profuse, then a coagulum moves forward, and closes up the aperture; it maintains for a few hours, sometimes for a day or two, its place, and then escapes; again the bleeding is renewed, and as now, the sore has enlarged, it is more impetuous than at first. Perhaps, a large coagulum or pressure on the opening, may once more save the patient from instant death, but it is only to protract his sufferings for a very limited time; for soon the hæmorrhage recurs, the extremities become cold, and the patient faints from loss of blood, never to revive; but in other cases he dies from hectic, before the sac actually gives way.

As the tumor enlarges, it produces in many cases, very serious symptoms; in others, the effects produced, bear no proportion to the extent of the disease. Where the aneurism does produce obvious signs of disease, you will find that the symptoms at first resemble those attending an irritable state of the heart. There is uneasiness in the chest, irregular action of the heart, generally referred to palpitation, together with dyspnœa, which is increased sometimes to a very alarming degree by exercise. In other cases, there is a short stiffling, teasing cough, accompanied with a mucous, or in some instances, with a bloody expectoration. Other patients again are free from the cough, but have a constant tendency to syncope, and some complain most bitterly of a working and beating about the thorax. Not a few experience a most oppressive feeling of weight or constriction about the heart, and are incessantly tormented with furious pulsation in the carotid arteries. The state of the pulse is extremely variable; sometimes it is " hard, slow, and chord- " like;" at other times, it is " small, and trem- " mulous;" occasionally, it is " feeble, and inter- " mittent;" sometimes the pulse in the two arms is not alike; in one case, " *pulsus in* " *brachio sinistro vehemens et intermittens ex-* " *plorabatur, in dextro vero exilis et obscurus* " *animadvertibatur.*" In another patient, " *pul-* " *sus brachii dextri exiguus et debilis exploraba-* " *tur; obscurior erat in brachio sinistro.*"

IN a history recorded by Barrher, the pulse was hard and intermittent. In one of Morgagni's cases, the pulse was quick and hard. These different conditions of the pulse were, in some of the cases, dependent on the combination of some affection of the heart, or large vessels with the aneurism; and in others, was referable to the position of the tumor, and its mechanical effects on the neighbouring parts. In the history re-

corded by Barrher, the tumor was seated on
the descending thoracic aorta : and in this patient, you would observe, it is mentioned that
the pulse was hard and intermittent. This observation of the state of the pulse is corroborated by what took place in two patients whom
I had an opportunity of seeing, with a similar disease. In other patients, in whom the ascending aorta had been aneurismal, the pulse
has had something of the feel that it communicates in pneumonia ; and in those instances,
where the pulse at the two wrists have been
unequal, you may, by reviewing the history of
the morbid phenomena observed on dissection,
discover the cause of inequality to have originated from the mechanical effect of the tumor.

IN many patients who have had aneurism of
the aorta, there has been a most distressing dysphagia for a length of time before death. As
we shall afterward see, when detailing cases,
this symptom most generally forms a prominent
feature in the complaint, when the disease is
seated about the arch of the aorta. Some patients are, for weeks, or even months before
death, hoarse, and obliged to speak in an under-
tone and rough voice ; and in not a few, there
are as in some diseases of the heart, œdema of
the face, turgescence of its veins, and feeling of
weight, or ringing in the head, together with
pain extending along the neck, and over the
shoulders, or even fixed in some distant part.

Dr. Simmons, in detailing the history of a case of aneurism of the aorta, states, that the patient complained of a " most painful spasm in the di-" rection of the diaphragm, which he compared " to a rope drawn tight round his chest." In some patients, there is, as in Syncope Anginosa, a troublesome degree of flatulence in the stomach and bowels, and in some, the symptoms are mitigated by the expulsion of wind from the stomach.

THE symptoms, which have just been enumerated, are often present where the tumor has not become so large as to appear externally; but I would give you a most imperfect view of the affection, if I did not inform you, that in many instances, it has proceeded a very great length, while the symptoms have been in no degree proportioned to the extent of organic derangement. Sometimes it even happens that the patients die from the rupture of the sac, where no serious disease had been suspected.

IN one case, which I dissected, where the tumor was about twice the size of a billiard-ball, and where it was attached by a short thick neck to the right side of the ascending aorta, just where it begins to form the curvature, I ascertained that no one had previously believed that the young woman was unwell. When I removed the sternum, the pericardium immediately came into view, very much distended, and of an extremely dark purple colour; it was so tense, that, when I made a small opening into it, blood,

partly coagulated, began to spout out. By slit-
ing it fully up, we removed all the coagula, and
exposed the tumor which was found to have
ruptured by a very small ragged aperture on its
most prominent point. We next cut open the
sound artery, opposite to the side where the tumor was placed, when we found that, between
the sac and the aorta, there was merely an aperture about sufficient to allow the passage of
the finger, and, by subsequent dissection, we ascertained that the cyst was entirely formed by
the dilated, and diseased cellular coat, and pericardium. The lacerated inner-coats, formed a
perforated septum between the vessel and the
sac, which, on its inner surface, was studded
over with white scales; some cartilaginous,
others bony, and it was also lined with shreds
of coagulating lymph. By passing the probe
from the sac through the aperture, the rupture
was found to have taken place near to the point
where the pericardium is reflected from the aorta, to form the loose capsule of the heart.

THESE appearances would surely lead us to believe, that the disease had existed for a considerable length of time, yet the patient, till the morning preceding her death, seemed to be in perfect
health; she rose, as usual, about seven o'clock,
and went about her household business till eight,
when she told a girl near her, that she did not
feel herself perfectly well; she complained of a
slight degree of nausea, and coldness about the

region of the heart. For an hour, she remained
much in the same state, then she suddenly
sprung from her seat, threw herself on the bed,
and hastily said, that she was very giddy, and
felt as if a cord was tied round the heart. This
was all she uttered, for before any of her companions could reach her, she was dead.

WE often meet with sudden death in those
who have small aneurismal tumors on the aorta,
but in this patient, you have seen, that the tumor was large; I may therefore mention, that,
in other two cases which I have seen, the tumor was as large, and seated precisely in the
same place, and the patients had no other
symptoms of disease, except a slight dyspnœa.

FROM the tumor, in all these three cases, being in precisely the same part of the artery, it
is more than probable, that the absence of the
characteristic signs of aneurism, arose from the
peculiarity in the position of the sac. We
examined one of them with great care, and
found, that the sac extended to the right of the
trachea, so that both it, and the gullet had escaped much pressure. It is only however when
the tumor grows out from the right side of the
ascending aorta, that this can occur; where it
originates from the front of the aorta, it presses
directly on the wind-pipe, producing very distressing dyspnœa. In these three cases, there
was no complaint made of beating about the
breast; and in all of them, death came sud-

denly, and very unexpectedly; which I must state, is always the case, when the rupture takes place within the pericardium. Every drop of blood which is, on each successive action of the heart forced through the rent, encroaches on the heart, oppresses its action, and prevents its due degree of distension, producing a feeling as if a cord were tied about this organ. From what we have seen, I would believe, that death is almost instantaneous after the real bursting of the sac. In the case which I have detailed at length, you would observe, that, for an hour before the patient died, there were unusual feelings in the chest, but I hardly think, that the sac had, till she sprung from her seat, actually given way: the fibres had, before that, probably begun to tear, but whenever the opening penetrated fully into the cyst, the person instantly expired.

THE dissection of these cases corroborates the theory of Scarpa; respecting the proximate cause of aneurism; for you have had occasion to notice that, in them the cyst originated from the lateral part of the artery, and was formed by an enlargement of the external cellular coat, and the pericardium, while the ruptured internal coats formed a perforated septum between the cavity of the sac, and the undiseased portion of the artery; and here, as in most cases of aneurism, the inner surface of the sac was covered over with scales of bone, and flakes of lymph, and by dissection we found, that between the cellular coat, which was thick and dense, and the pericardium, there was a new layer of pulpy matter deposited. In two of them the pericardium was more affected than in the third, but in all it is to be observed, that the rupture did not appear to be occasioned by a sphacelation of the cyst, but by actual laceration, which will generally be found to be the case when an internal aneurism gives way. When, however, an external aneurism bursts, it is generally by reason, as Mr. S. Cooper remarks, of a sloughing of its coverings.

I AM happy to have it in my power, to corroborate what has been mentioned respecting the ambiguity of the symptoms produced by aneurism of the thoracic aorta, by the case related in the following very valuable communication, for which I am indebted to the friendship of Mr. Astley Cooper, of London. To this case, Mr. Cooper has had the goodness to add a list of the operations he has performed for the cure of external aneurisms. Their results, whether successful or the reverse, have been impartially stated, and the causes of failure mentioned. This detail, therefore, cannot fail to be read with great interest. It is intended to shew, that although internal aneurisms may in some patients be conjoined with external, that still combination is by no means so frequent, as to afford any reasonable objection to the performance of an operation for the removal of the latter. The fact is, that unless where an operation is obviously prohibited by the unequivocal existence of an internal aneurism, we are, if the patient be otherwise in a favourable state, to attempt the cure of any external aneurism by operation. If the operation prove sometimes unsuccessful, from the rupture of an undiscovered internal aneurism, this circumstance cannot surely either be brought forward as an objection to the operation, or laid to the charge of the operator. It argues no neglect or deficiency on the part of the operator; for it may happen, in the practice of the most intelligent, as readily, as in that of the most ignorant. It is an event, which in general the most consummate knowledge can neither foresee nor prevent.

MR. COOPER'S Case. " George Stephens, " aged forty-two years, applied to me on the " 26th of October, on account of a popliteal " aneurism. It began two months ago, in a pain- " ful sensation in stretching his leg; and when " the knee was rested on the edge of a chair or " bed, he felt a pulsation in the ham, but has " only discovered the swelling about a fort- " night. He has now violent and constant pain " from the calf of the leg to the ancle, and " the latter is swollen. He says, that he is " otherwise in good health, and attributes the " disease to his excessive labour, being accus-

" tomed to carry heavy loads, and to walk
" twelve miles a-day."

" I INFORMED him of the dangerous nature
" of the disease, and advised him to become a
" patient in the hospital, to which he made no
" objection, and the following day he was ad-
" mitted into Guy's, and consented to the ope-
" ration, without shewing any extraordinary
" reluctance.

" HE placed himself upon the table, and I
" began the operation near the middle of the
" thigh, but before I had concluded my first in-
" cision, having only exposed some of the fibres
" of the sartorius muscle, his urine gushed from
" the urethra, and the lower extremities be-
" came stiffened. I immediately enquired how
" he felt himself, when looking at his face, it
" appeared livid, his breathing had stopt, and
" his pulse was extremely feeble. In about a
" minute he breathed; air was admitted about
" him ; I opened a vein in his arm, but it would
" not bleed; I opened the jugular vein, and he
" bled about three ounces; his pulse became
" weaker, but he breathed again ; I pressed up-
" on the chest, and suffered it to expand by
" its elasticity; he again breathed, a pair of
" bellows were brought, and the lungs were in-
" flated, his face became paler; his pulse was
" scarcely perceptible ; he breathed once more
" and expired.

" As this unexpected event had happened

" before a number of medical students and
" others, and the cause of his death was very
" inexplicable, I requested them to meet me at
" the same hour on the following day, that I
" might in their presence inspect the body.

" The brain, which was first examined, was
" perfectly sound. The abdominal viscera were
" also free from disease, but when the chest was
" opened, the pericardium projected more than
" usual, and appeared of a leaden colour. When
" this was opened, it was found filled with a
" large mass of coagulated blood, and upon
" tracing the source of this, an aneurism of
" that part of the aorta which is covered by
" the pericardium, was found projecting over
" the superior cava, with an opening in it as
" large as a goose quill, into the pericardium.

" As the man expressed himself to have been
" perfectly well in his general health, I was
" anxious to learn what symptoms he had of
" this disease, and his wife only replied to my
" inquiries in this respect, that for a month
" past, after eating, he said, ' *he felt a load at
" the pit of his stomach;*" as if his digestion
" was imperfect; and that if he exerted himself
" during the last fortnight, his breathing was
" quicker than usual, which he attributed to
" the pain which he suffered in his leg, whilst
" walking. These were the only symptoms of
" aortic aneurism I could collect.

" As a case of this kind might prejudice the

" minds of some persons, against the operation
" for aneurism generally, I have subjoined the
" cases on which I have operated."

" POPLITEAL ANEURISM."

" EDWARD POWELL, aged twenty-seven;
" operation, April 1802; now resides in Lon-
" don."

" HENRY FIGG, aged twenty-nine; operation
" in May 1802; at present resides near Rei-
" gate, Surrey; a patient of Mr. Martin's of
" Reigate."

" JAMES CHAPMAN, aged fifty-two; opera-
" tion in the summer of 1802; now a servant
" to the treasurer of Guy's hospital."

" ———— CUTHBERTSON, aged thirty; ope-
" ration in 1803; now a coal porter in Lon-
" don."

" ———— CAMPBELL, aged twenty-six; ope-
" ration in 1804; died in six weeks after. On
" examination, water was found in the pericar-
" dium, and an aneurism at the root of the me-
" senteric artery. The aorta was found much
" diseased."

" A. B. sent into Guy's hospital by Mr.
" Holt, Surgeon of Westminster; operation in
" August 1805; died at Christmas of the same
" year, in consequence of suppuration of the
" aneurismal sac."

" ROBERT DARLING, a patient of Messrs.
" Horsford and Hopke's, Ratcliffe Highway;

" operation in 1806; recovered; he went into
" the north of England, since which, I have had
" no account of him."

" A. B. a patient of Mr. Jones of Deptford;
" operation in 1806; died at sea, 15 months
" afterwards; cause of his death unknown."

" —— JONES, a patient of Mr. Holt of
" Tottenham; died three weeks after the ope-
" ration, with symptoms of tetanus."

" Mr. —— FOX, aged sixty-nine, a patient
" of Mr. Butler, Hoxton; operation in March,
" 1808; now lives in Bath, St. Hackney Road."

" WILLIAM GOLDRING, operation in May
" 1808, in Guy's hospital; discharged cured."

" FEMORAL ANEURISM."

" A. B. a patient in Guy's Hospital, sent to
" me out of Buckinghamshire; femoral artery
" tied within two inches of Paupart's ligament;
" soon recovered, and I heard several months
" afterwards that he was perfectly well."

" INGUINAL ANEURISM."

" A. B. a patient in Guy's Hospital, whose
" leg had been amputated above the knee,
" some years before; operation for aneurism
" performed by tying the femoral artery under
" Paupart's ligament, and above the Arteria
" Profunda; a single ligature only was used;
" this man died of hœmorrhage, fourteen days
" after the operation."

" JOHN COWLES, aged thirty-two; operation

" in June 1808; he recovered but very slowly;
" he is now living in Beccles, in Suffolk."

" CAROTID ANEURISM."

" MARY EDWARDS, aged forty-four; opera-
" tion in November 1805; died on the twenty-
" third day after the operation, from inflamma-
" tion in the aneurismal sac, both ligatures
" came away on the twelfth day."

" HUMPHREY HUMPHRIES, aged fifty; ope-
" ration in June 1808; he is perfectly recover-
" ed, and now resides in Labour-in-vain Court,
" near Bread Street Hill, London."

" POSTERIOR AURAL ANEURISM."

" A. B. a patient of Mr. Fry's of Dursley,
" Glocestershire; operation performed; I heard
" from Mr. F. some years afterwards, that this
" woman was perfectly well."

THE same ambiguity of symptoms will be
well illustrated by the following case drawn up
by my brother:

Mr. JOHN BURNS' Case. " A literary gen-
" tleman, of a stout muscular make, rather
" inclined to obesity, consulted me on the
" 30th of January last, respecting a peculiar
" sensation he occasionally felt in the left side,
" and which he observed, was attended by an
" irregularity and occasional intermission of
" the pulse. He was about fifty-six years of
" age, enjoyed excellent health, had a good

" appetite, and remarked that he had not been
" a day confined for a great many years. This
" sensation, of which he complained, went off
" soon, but returned about the 27th of March;
" he was bled, and directed to keep the bowels
" open, to avoid fermented liquors, to live ra-
" ther sparingly, and particularly never to
" make a full meal. Through the summer, he
" enjoyed good health, but felt slight diffi-
" culty of breathing when he walked fast, and
" occasionally he expectorated mucus mix-
" ed with a little blood.

" ON the 5th of December, 1808, having
" been fatigued through the day, and having
" attended the funeral of a particular friend,
" he was seized immediately after dinner with
" a sudden sensation about the sternum, as if
" a bone had stuck in his throat; his eyes
" stared, and he became very faint. I saw him
" in the course of ten minutes after, and found
" him sitting in a chair, his countenance ghast-
" ly, his hands cold, his pulse irregular, and
" so weak, as sometimes to be imperceptible.
" Just as I came in, he vomited a little, and
" was immediately helped to bed; in the course
" of an hour, he vomited again, and felt some-
" what relieved, but the pulse still remain-
" ed small like a thread. Next day he felt
" so much better, that it was with difficulty
" he was persuaded to keep the house. He
" complained still however of a little uneasi-

" ness about the lower part of the sternum; and
" the pulse, though now firm, was irregular.

" ON the 9th, he went to bed in his usual
" health, but got up about four o'clock next
" morning: He soon returned to bed, and was
" observed to breath heavily; his wife raised
" him up, but he had by that time expired,
" without a groan.   A servant supporting him
" behind, thought she heard something crack
" about his back."

" DISSECTION.—When the thorax was open-
" ed, the pericardium was found gorged with
" coagulated blood, and with bloody serum.
" The whole of the heart was fat and flabby,
" and so soft, that the finger, could with the
" greatest ease be pushed through its sub-
" stance. The right side of this organ was di-
" lated to a considerable degree, and the auri-
" cle just where its lap folds over the root of
" the aorta, had ruptured. On examining the
" aorta, we found the pericardiac and cellular
" covering of the ascending part of this ves-
" sel, very considerably thickened, and on its
" anterior face, they were separated from the
" proper coats, from the root of the aorta up to
" the origin of the arteria anonyma.   A large
" aneurismal sac was thus formed between the
" proper and cellular coverings. The base of
" the sac was every where defined by a firm
" union of the external to the fibrous coats. On
" tearing this adhesion, an indurated elevated

" line of whitish matter was left attached to
" the internal coats. By slitting open the pos-
" terior side of the aorta, an irregular rent of
" about half an inch in length, was brought
" into view, formed in the proper coats on the
" front of the artery. Through this aperture, the
" blood had passed from the proper canal of the
" aorta, into the aneurismal cyst. The fibrous
" coats were along the whole extent of the as-
" cending aorta, somewhat dilated, and the
" artery itself was very much diseased, even
" to where it gives off the iliac vessels. In
" many parts, there were plates of bone, more
" than a line in thickness, interposed between
" the tunics, and in two spots, we found fungi
" several lines in thickness, contained between
" the internal and middle coats."

THE preceding case is in many respects curious, and it is interesting, both on account of the
insidious progress of the disease, the mildness
of the symptoms, and the complete and satisfactory explanation of these afforded by the inspection of the body. When we review the
morbid phenomena, and compare them with the
symptoms, we cannot fail to be struck with the
correspondence. The dilatation of the right
side of the heart, affords an explanation of the
expectoration of blood, and the slight difficulty
of breathing he experienced when walking fast,
or otherwise exerting himself. The flabbiness
and weakness of the muscular substance, ac-

counts for the irregularity and intermission of the pulse ; and the state of the aorta and right auricle, will explain the nature of the paroxysm he had on the 5th of December, and elucidate the immediate cause of death. From a review of the symptoms he had on the Monday preceding his death, there can remain little doubt, that at the time he sprung from his seat, the partially dilated proper coats of the artery had given way. As, however, the blood was still confined in a circumscribed cyst, the circulation, when the first shock was over, returned to as natural a standard as was compatible with the morbid state of the heart and arteries. The vascular system remained languid, the person was easily fatigued, and at last on the Friday morning, after slight exertion, the auricle ruptured; blood was poured out between the pericardium and the heart, and this almost instantaneously, from the ticklish condition of the circulating system, proved fatal.

PROFESSOR SCARPA records a case where a small aneurism had formed on the root of the aorta, and gave way without the existence of any symptoms which could indicate the presence of such a disease. The patient, " Joseph Varani, " 22 years of age, a corporal of the 4th com- " pany of pioneers, while he was conversing " cheerfully with his companions, was struck " suddenly dead. This man, formerly by trade " a shoemaker, had been repeatedly infected

" with lues venerea, and had also several times
" undergone a mercurial course; he had never,
" however, complained of difficulty of breath-
" ing, and his pulse had never been found ir-
" regular or intermitting, not even a few weeks
" before his death. On examining his body, the
" pericardium immediately presented itself quite
" distended with blood; the aorta, in the vici-
" nity of the heart, at the distance of half an
" inch above its valves, where it began to be
" incurvated, presented externally, a tumor of
" the size of a nut, which opened by a small
" hole within the pericardium." The Professor
proceeds to describe the appearances presented
by a careful examination of the tumour, but in
this detail, it is not necessary to follow him.

THIS case illustrates most satisfactorily, the
fact of the suddenness of death, in those instances
where the sac bursts within the pericardium.
But in two cases, I have found the death as instantaneous, where the tumour was very small,
and where it had not ruptured.

THE first case, was one which I was requested to inspect about five years ago. The
subject was a young woman, who had in the
early part of her life been rather dissolute, but
for some months before her death, her friends
believed that she had become more regular.
She never complained of any pain, or beating
about the breast; neither had she ever had
any difficulty in breathing; she had rather

been uncommonly healthy, and the day on which she died, she had set out on a journey on foot, and had proceeded for about ten miles, when she suddenly sat down, and in a few minutes expired. We expected to have found some rupture of the heart or vessels, but after a very careful search, we could not discover any disease about the heart; we saw at the root of the aorta, a protuberance about the size of a musket ball. We cut into this, and found it hollow, and separated from the canal of the artery, by a septum formed by the internal coats of the vessel, which were perforated by a small puckered opening, not larger than the barrel of a goose quill. We opened the canal of the aorta, and found on this side, that the septum between the sac and the vessel was smooth, and exactly resembling the natural appearance of the villous coat, except about the edges of the opening, where it was puckered and thickened. On the other side, the septum was rough, and covered over with coagulating lymph. We brought away the parts with us, that we might have a better opportunity of examining the structure of the outer coverings of the sac. We dissected these, and found them to consist of the cellular coat, which was thickened, and which at the root of the cyst, adhered firmly to the internal coats, so as to confine the blood, and define the swelling. The pericardium over the tumour was very little thickened. On examining the uterus, we found it in the first stage of pregnancy.

THE next case which I saw of this kind, so nearly resembles this, that I do not consider it necessary to state the particulars. I must however mention, that the tumour was about the size of a pigeon's egg, and had not given way; the uterus was also in the early stage of gravidity. I relate these, as cases of sudden death from similar causes may often be met with in the course of practice; and in diseases of the heart occurring in those who are in the early stage of pregnancy, you will find the fatal issue take place at a period when, without the induction of the uterine action, it would not in all probability have happened.

I HAVE had an opportunity of dissecting several cases of this kind, and have even found an affection of the aortic valves, which, without the co-operation of the peculiar state of the womb, was not so far advanced as to carry off the patient. I do not pretend to explain, how in such cases, pregnancy accelerates death. I only state a fact, proved by experience: when called to examine those who have died suddenly, you will find on inspecting the body, the heart or large vessels in a state of disease, yet not so far advanced, as to account for death. On examining the womb, it will be discovered, that the uterine system has been in a state of excitement. Sometimes you will find it in the first stage of pregnancy. In four cases of diseased heart, where death had taken place unexpectedly, I found the uterus gravid; in two others, the patients had been menstruating. But it must also be mentioned, that in both of these, the catameniæ had for some time before been suppressed. How the excitation of the specific action of the uterus should produce death in such cases, is in the present state of our knowledge perhaps inexplicable: We see, however, other examples, in which disease of the heart produces a morbid effect on the womb.

WHEN treating of chronic inflammation of the heart, I might have informed you, that when this condition occurs in a pregnant woman, the uterus generally expels the fœtus prematurely; we cannot however assign any probable reason, why it should do so, neither can we explain how, when pregnancy takes place in a female with incipient aneurism of the aorta, death in some cases occurs without the sac being burst. We see that it is so, but why it is so, we cannot say. If in such cases, the sac had ruptured, we might perhaps discover a cause for this occurrence in the state of the system accompanying gravidity; but in fact, the aneurism seldom gives way, death taking place before the disease has proceeded so far as to permit this event.

HAVING now finished the general history of aneurism of the thoracic aorta, I may, to illustrate the complaint, select a few histories from among the different cases on record, and add a few of my own.

MORGAGNI, in Epist. 17th, and Art. 14th, records a case in which the patient had a teazing cough, accompanied with bloody expectoration. This person complained also for a length of time, of oppressive pain in the chest, and at the time of quick motion, he was seized with a difficult respiration, and that pain in the thorax, mentioned formerly, sometimes also with a palpitation of the heart, which obliged him to stand still; these symptoms were much relieved by eructation. Although Morgagni says nothing of the state of the valves of the heart, referring the whole of the previous symptoms to an extensive aneurism of the descending thoracic aorta, and the death to a rupture of the sac, yet I may call your attention to the similarity of the symptoms to those attendant on diseased aortic valves. Indeed, had there been no aneurism present, no one, from a perusal of the history, could have doubted that the symptoms had entirely originated from a morbid state of the valves.

IN the seventeenth article of the same letter, you will find the history of another case of aneurism of the thoracic aorta, " in which, on using " exercise, the patient experienced very great " difficulty in breathing, and anguish at his " heart. The carotid and temporal arteries " had evidently a leaping motion, the pulse

" was hard, rather slow, and chord-like, but
" never intermitting, nor unequal." Towards
the close of life, the face became œdematous,
and he had frequent returns of syncope.

IN another patient who died from aneurism
of the ascending aorta, the disease was accompanied with a wheezing, difficulty of breathing,
sense of stricture about the præcordia, occasional paroxysms of violent pain in the loins,
strong pulsation of the carotid arteries, and
bloody expectoration. It is to be regretted, that
in this case, owing to the putridity of the body,
Valsalva and Morgagni did not judge it proper
to examine the abdomen, but the former anatomist believed that there was no organic disease
about the loins. If this had been ascertained,
it would have made a valuable addition to the
history of this case; for it would have shewn,
that reference of the pain to a distant part, is
not confined to diseases of the heart, but also
accompanies affections of the large vessels.

IN the case of the Marquis Paulucci, where
the disease was supposed to be brought on by
passion, the symptoms were more severe than
they usually are ; " he could neither lie down, nor
" go to stool, nor make water, nor even swal-
" low nourishment, but almost immediately a
" paroxysm was brought on which threatened
" instant suffocation, and even death itself;
" he used sometimes to leap suddenly out of
" the seat, on which to avoid all motion, he

" continually sat, and ran to the window, with
" the hopes of breathing better there; yet, ne-
" vertheless, he used to draw his breath with a
" stertor, to be livid in the face, to discharge
" his urine and fœces involuntarily, which cir-
" cumstance very frequently happened. Some-
" times the stricture upon his heart, was so
" great, that his breath being quite intercepted,
" he could not even move, but fell forwards,
" upon the arms of his servants, who supported
" him on each side, like one about to expire."
Morgagni expresses his regret that he had it
not in his power to be present at the dissection
of this Nobleman, but he informs us, that an
aneurismal tumour was found at the curvature
of the aorta, " of the bigness of a kid's head."
It is however unfortunate that we have no accurate history of the precise spot where the
tumour was placed; had this been stated, we
might perhaps have been able to trace the
reason of the unusual difficulty in breathing
and the lividity of the face. I myself have
met with one instance in some respects similar
to that of the Marquis Paulucci, for on using
exercise, the countenance became dark, and
the breathing was almost suspended; effects
produced as we shall afterwards see, by the pressure of the tumour on the trachea. Morgagni
conjectures, that in the Marquis P. the dyspnœa
in the supine posture, was induced by the
weight of the tumour forcing the trachea against

the spine. Had the relation of the sac to the
wind-pipe been explicitly stated, we could
readily have been able to ascertain what effect
the gravitation of the aneurism would have on
the Aspera arteria. In some cases of aortic
aneurism, we see a very decided effect produced
by the tumour interrupting the entrance of the
air; but in others, where the sac is seen so large
as to have appeared externally after breaking
open the chest, we witness, comparatively speaking, little effect produced on the respiratory
function. There must be some physical reason for this diversity of effect.

In the 18th Lett. and 16th Art. it is recorded, that the patient after having been for about
a year troubled with a severe and almost incessant cough, accompanied with dyspnœa,
" when he went up steep places," was seized
suddenly, " in the middle of the night, with
" such an oppressive torture at his breast, that
" he was afraid of immediate suffocation." This.
patient had, in addition to these symptoms, an
occasional sensation, as of a cord binding the
trachea, he became emaciated, but his pulse
continued regular. At last, on the 70th day
from the beginning of the urgent symptoms, he
died.

It may be worthy of observation, that in
this person, there was on the aorta, where it
arose from the heart, a large aneurismal sac, so
capacious as to contain a pound of blood. I

may also point out the resemblance of this case, to that last detailed. There was the same difficulty of breathing, the same oppression in the chest, the same effects produced by the pressure of the tumour on the trachea in the supine position. This patient, like the Marquis Paulucci, was compelled to sit erect, and to have ease in breathing, he was even necessitated to incline forwards. You will thus trace at once, the resemblance of this to the last case, and here we do not require to regret the want of precision in the statement of the locality of the tumour. We have it explicitly mentioned, that " in the aorta, where it arose from the " heart, a great aneurism was seen." We see here, that the aneurism was seated in the ascending aorta; this I would have you particularly remark, for in our cases, where the disease has been seated in this portion of the artery, we have found the symptoms much more severe, than when the arch of the aorta was aneurismal.

From a review of the cases, which I find in practical works of aortic aneurism, I am inclined to think, that when the ascending aorta is aneurismal, the breathing is more affected than when the arch of the vessel is enlarged; but in the latter case, you have to observe, that deglutition is more impaired than in the former. Those who know the relation of the ascending aorta to the trachea, and are able to trace the

connection of the arch of the aorta with the
œsophagus, will anticipate me in the explanation. It will be recollected, that the ascending aorta, crosses the root of the aspera arteria,
while the arch is more over the œsophagus;
hence, if the tumour juts out from the top of
the curvature, and extends to the left, it must
rather affect the gullet than the windpipe. It
must however be demonstrable, that although
the faculty of swallowing be more impaired
than the function of respiration, that yet in
every case where a serious degree of dysphagia
is induced, there must be a greater or less share
of dyspnœa present. The 22d article in Morgagni's 18th letter, is an excellent illustration of
these facts. He relates, that in a Trumpeter,
an aneurism occupied the upper and internal
parts of the chest. The tumour increased slowly in size, and as it became bigger, the deglutition became more and more difficult, and the
oppression in breathing increased.

THE author adds, the dysphagia first became
complete, and then the dyspnœa increasing in
severity, the patient was carried off: Starvation
would have killed him independent of suffocation. On opening this body, the curvature of
the aorta was found aneurismal.

IN the 804 Observation of Lieutaud, will be
found the history of a case of aneurism of the
arch of the aorta, accompanied with difficulty
in breathing and swallowing. The 824 Obser-

vation, is a case, where from the top of the arch of the aorta, an aneurismal sac arose as large as an egg. In this person, " *aderat dysp-* " *nœa cum tussi levi, et difficile deglutitione tan-* " *dem interiit.*" Were it necessary, I could mention other cases, to prove, that when the arch of the aorta is affected with aneurism, the patients generally suffer more from dyspha- gia, than from difficulty in breathing, although they also unquestionably find the latter symp- tom very distressing. In those cases however, where the ascending aorta is aneurismal, we shall find that the patients are more distressed by difficulty in breathing, than in swallowing. One case to which I formerly alluded, affords a sufficient example of this.

THE patient was a man, robust and athletic, and by trade a wright. Till toward the latter part of his life, he had been remarkably heal- thy, having hardly ever known what it was to be confined by illness. About twelve months before his death, he began suddenly, after fa- tigue in lifting wood, during a severe thun- der storm, to be rather subject to complaints; yet they were at first so slight, that except when he had been exerting himself, he could hardly define his symptoms. He was indeed easily fatigued, but he ate and slept well; when however, he walked fast, or fatigued him- self by working, or was in a passion, he never failed to bring on such a fit of breathlessness, and sense of suffocation, as compelled him to lay himself along on a bench, or on the ground, where, after resting for half an hour, he got up much relieved. When I inform you, that for nearly a month before his death, he had dyspnœa brought on by more trivial causes than formerly ; and if I add, that on attempting to raise a very heavy piece of wood, he suddenly felt faintish, with an indescribable feeling of constriction in the chest, and that he threw himself on his back on a bed, where he instantly expired ; I mention the only facts in his history, which are worth the relating.

ON dissection we found, that the heart was much enlarged, its sides very thin, and its surface loaded with fat. The veins and pulmonary artery were healthy, but the aorta, from its root to its arch, was aneurismal ; not a partial growth from its side, but a fair enlargement of the complete circumference of the vessel, producing a huge pyriform cyst: This enlargement might be supposed to be a simple dilatation of the coats of the artery, but in reality the sac had all the the characters of true aneurism. The pericardium, and coats beneath it, were thickened and altered in their texture. They had assumed a pulpy gelatinous appearance, and on the inner surface of the bag, there was a coating of coagulating lymph, intermixed with scales of bone. The tumour lay just over the bifurcation of the windpipe, and it was so large, that when its cavity was inflated, it forced the trachea against the spine. The enlargement occupied all the ascending part of the aorta, but about the arch, the dilated part slowly and almost imperceptibly declined into the sound portion of the vessel. On examining the condition of the arterial valves, we found that they were thickened, and in part ossified; and also, we saw the coronary arteries of the heart in some measure diseased; they were denser, and less elastic than usual, but they were not in a state of actual ossification.

THIS case, at the same time that it shews the effect produced on the breathing by an aneurism on the ascending aorta, is also in many other respects worthy of attention. It must recal to your memory, the history of the Marquis Paulucci, to which, in many respects, it bears a near resemblance, only in our case, the fate of the man was more early decided than in the Italian Nobleman. This may perhaps have been owing to the co-operation of the diseased coronary arteries and ossified valves; or perhaps it may have been dependent on the person having less attention paid to his conveniency and comfort. Had the Marquis Paulucci been obliged to earn his bread by hard labour, his disease in all probability, would not have been so protracted. In this respect, I think our patient had the more desirable fate of the two. Morgagni, in the history of the symptoms accompanying the aneurism in the Marquis Paulucci, has observed, that when he lay supine, the tumour by its pressure on the trachea, produced such a feeling of suffocation, as obliged the patient to raise himself, and even to stoop forward. In our case, the man, while nearly in a fit of syncope, threw himself on his back along the bed, so that the tumour must have continued to compress the trachea, and thus perhaps the apparent death was sooner converted into real death than otherwise would have been the case. In the present instance, I think there is no doubt, but that during exertion, the aneurismal cyst had become so tense, as to press the trachea against the spine, and this taken into account with the state of the valves and nutrient vessels of the heart, is sufficient to explain the faintishness, difficulty of breathing, and oppression felt in the chest.

AFTER this case, I may bring forward the twenty-eighth article of the eighteenth book of Morgagni's Epistles, which contains the history of a complicated case, but one which nevertheless will illustrate and impress on the mind the general fact which I have stated. The patient was an octodenarian who often complained of her stomach, which it seems in the language of her country, meant the lower part of the thorax. This patient was most dreadfully distressed with difficulty in breathing, and was compelled, in order to avoid actual suffocation,

to sit erect; " her pulse was tense and cord-like."
After a length of suffering, she died from suffocation.

THE heart was enlarged and thickened in its
parietes, which, if it be recollected what was
stated to be the consequence of solid increase of
the substance of the heart, will account for the
state of the pulse: The never ceasing oppression in breathing, is clearly explained by the
state of the aorta. This vessel " was greatly di-
" lated, quite from the heart, even to the first
" orifice of its superior branches;" and here,
I would have you particularly notice the description which the accurate author gives of the
state of the sac internally.   He represents it as
studded over with bony scales, which he com-
pares to drops of white wax, after they are
cooled on the floor.   This conveys a most accurate idea of the appearance of the scales of
bone which are found in an aneurismal sac; the
semi-opaque white on the dark ground is a very
happy illustration.   Ruysch records a case of
a very large aneurism of the ascending aorta;
so large, as to have made its way through the
thorax, appearing externally where it formed a tumour as big as the head, and pulsating
for many weeks with great fury. This aneurism gave rise to great oppression in breathing,
a febrile state of the system, and frequent attacks of syncope; at last, exhausted by hectic
and pain, the patient died.

IN the first volume of the Medical Communications, there is a valuable history of a case of aneurism of the aorta, written by Dr. Simmons. In this patient, the symptoms were similar to those which often attend this disease which was seated in the ascending aorta. He breathed with extreme difficulty, was tormented with a teasing cough; " his face was livid and " and bloated, his pulse in each wrist, was " small, and with difficulty to be felt, and his " hands and feet were slightly œdematous." He complained likewise of " a most painful spasm " in the direction of the diaphragm, which he " compared to a rope drawn tight round his " chest." During the continuance of this stricture, he was obliged to lean forward, in order to procure ease in breathing; toward the close of his life, all his symptoms increased in severity, but the spasm and difficulty in breathing were still the most prominent features in his complaint.

" THE aorta began to be preternaturally di- " lated a little above its origin from the heart, " but the aneurismal sac appears to have been " formed by a partial dilatation of that artery, " at the anterior part of its curvature, for the " ascending branches are seen contiguous to " each other, though somewhat larger than " usual."

BETWEEN the sac and the spine, the vena cava was found, adhering to the former, and very much compressed.

Dr. SIMMONS, in his remarks on this history, observes, " It corroborates the observations " made by Ruysch and Littre; that an aneurism " of the aorta may exist in a considerable de-" gree, with little or no pulsation, and that the " pulsation may become obscure in proportion " as the firmness of the coagulum in the sac in-" creases."

" THE relief which the patient experienced in his breathing, by leaning forward, is like-wise a circumstance worthy of attention. The same thing was observed by Morgagni, in a si-milar case where the aneurismal sac pressed on the vena cava superior."

You will, no doubt, from what you know of this disease, anticipate a remark which I would make on this conjecture of the pressure of the sac on the vena cava, being the cause of the difficulty in breathing. You will readily understand from the part of the artery affected, that the trachea must have been very much pres-sed on; and it has already been mentioned, that difficulty in breathing is an almost invariable symptom produced by aneurism of this portion of the aorta. I would also call your attention to the stricture about the diaphragm, so much complained of by this patient, and probably oc-casioned by the aneurismal sac irritating the phrenic nerve. Dr. Simmons observes, that he had seen the same symptom in three cases of aneurism of the aorta, which had come under his care; and from this, he seems inclined to place some dependence on its occurrence, as affording assistance in distinguishing this affection from other diseases. I would, however, wish you to understand, that we cannot from the presence or absence of this symptom, form any opinion of the nature of the disease; we often meet with such a structure in morbid conditions of the heart, and in many patients, who have died from aneurism of the aorta, no sensation of this kind has ever been experienced. It can therefore by no means be considered, even when it accompanies other symptoms of disturbed respiration, and irregular circulation, " as an " additional clue to the diagnosis in these me- " lancholy cases."

THE cases which have just been recorded, will be sufficient to illustrate the general appearance which the disease presents. They shew, that in aneurism from the ascending aorta, the breathing is commonly very much affected, while they also prove, that when the curvature is aneurismal, the function of deglutition is more impaired than the respiratory process; although you must have observed, that the latter does not altogether escape.

FROM the general history of this disease, and from the detail of cases, you will have perceived, that in aneurism of the thoracic aorta, death may be produced either by the mechanical effect of the tumour on the neighbouring parts, or by rupture of the sac; or in a less obvious way, by some connection with pregnancy. You have seen in one case in particular, the death to be entirely dependant on the pressure of the enlargement of the ascending aorta on the trachea, and in others, you have observed, that although the tumour did give rise to considerable difficulty in breathing, that yet the death was more immediately referable to the dysphagia. In most of the cases however, the fatal issue was owing to rupture of the sac. In reviewing the cases on record of aneurism of the thoracic aorta, we find, that some of them had burst into the pericardium; others had made an opening into the trachea, and many had effused their contents into the general cavity of the thorax.

WHEN the tumour bursts within the pericardium for the reason which has already been mentioned, death instantly follows the rupture.

WHEN the tumour opens into the trachea, death is seldom protracted. " *Interea decem* " *elapsis mensibus incipit rejicere per tussim gru-* " *mos nigri et concreti sanguinis, unde tumor* " *multum imminuitur, sed cum continua esset san-* " *guinis excretio occubuit.*" " *Inter dissectionem* " *cadaveris, invenitur aorta descendens mire dila-* " *tata, cujus, scilicet, tanta erat amplitudo ut duas* " *sanguinis libras et ultra capere poscit. Hic tu-* " *mor ad latus asprece arterice exesus videbatur,* " *et hians in posticam partem prædicti tubi unde* " *lethalis sanguinis evacuatio.*" Where the sac bursts by a small opening into the general cavity of the chest, death takes place more slowly: In the former instances, you have seen the blood when effused into the pericardium, oppressing the heart, and in that way, destroying the patient; when also the blood escapes into the trachea, it obstructs the passage of the air, and thus speedily suffocates the person. By bursting into the thorax, death is as certainly, although rather more slowly produced. It sometimes likewise happens, that there is a tendency to the formation of a swelling on the side of the vessel by a lymphatic production, such as we see in cases where a large artery has been wounded, and the blood collected in a defined cyst.

IN Morgagni's seventeenth letter, and fourteenth article, we have a history of this kind. " The aneurism was ruptured, and had dis- " charged its blood by a large hiatus into the " left cavity of the thorax ; about this foramen, " there was a polypus concretion hollowed out " into the form of a little tube." This however can only take place where death does not for a few hours follow the rupture. With regard to the cause of death in cases of incipient aneurism, conjoined with pregnancy, we are yet altogether ignorant.

BEFORE concluding the history of aneurism of the aorta, I must caution you against mistaking every pulsating tumour about the top of chest for this disease. Some tumours evidently not aneurismal, assume so much of the appearance of this disease, that without a very careful examination, they are extremely apt to be considered as such.

I REMEMBER a case of a man in whom a pretty large pulsating tumour appeared from behind the sternal extremity of the left clavicle. It was bigger than a hen's egg, pulsated very strongly, and produced an irrregularity in the pulse at the wrist; great difficulty in swallowing, and a slight dyspnœa. The surgeon never doubted but that it was an aneurism; and accordingly, he explained to the man his danger, and the great risk which he would run of the tumour bursting, if he fatigued himself, or lived freely. On the faith of this, he prevailed on the patient to keep quiet in the house, and persuaded him to take great care of himself; and regularly once a day, for some months, he went to visit him. During all that time, the tumour did not enlarge, neither did the pulsation become either more violent or more obscure. This tedious restriction being not altogether to the patient's mind, and as he did not perceive that the danger was such as had been represented, he began to have an opinion of his own; he walked out, and ate and drank as plentifully as his means would permit, and found that the swelling, in place of enlarging, as had been predicted, really became smaller, the pulsation decreased in strength, and, in the end, to the astonishment of all who saw him, both the tumour and beating left him. You will, from the issue of this case, readily see that the disease could not be aneurism. The tumour, however, had so many of the characters of this complaint, that no one who saw the patient, had any doubt respecting the nature of the case. We must not, however, in every case, depend on the symptoms, for if we do, we shall often commit similar mistakes. It is necessary to recollect, that a gland enlarged over the seat of an artery, and in contact with the vessel, always pulsates more strongly than the artery beneath it. For this reason, I have more than once seen an enlarged lymphatic gland in the neck, mistaken for aneurism of the carotid artery: we can, however, at all times distinguish these pulsating glandular swellings from real aneurism.

IN real aneurism, we uniformly find, on the action of the sound artery behind it, the tumour enlarged, and rendered tense, but it soon decreases in size, and becomes softer; we find on grasping it, that its dimensions are, during the action of the vessel, increased all round, and by pulling it outward, we produce no change on the degree of beating. In the case however of a glandular swelling, placed over the tract of an artery, on grasping the tumour, we perceive that it only rises and falls during the systole and diastole of the vessel, its lateral diameter suffers no change, and by pulling it outward, we destroy altogether, or render its beating very obscure. Had we in this way, examined the case I have just described, we never could have been deceived; and had Dr. Heberden done the same, in the histories which he relates of pulsating tumours in the neck, he would have been enabled to have spoken more decidedly than he has done respecting the nature of these swellings. Morgagni observes, that in the advanced stage of aneurism, the pulsation sometimes disappears; and he adds, as there may be an aneurism of the aorta without pulsation, so there may be pulsation without an aneurism of the artery. You must therefore in deciding on the nature of a case, examine carefully the preceding and existing symptoms; and from a review of the history of the patient, you must judge whether the disease be really aneurism, or only a glandular tumour, resembling, in some respects, this disease.

THERE is another affection which presents some of the characters of aneurism of the arch of the aorta, and which occasionally perplexes the surgeon in his diagnosis. I allude to dilatation of the termination of the internal jugular vein. It is by no means a rare occurrence to meet with an enlargement of this part of the vein, especially in asthmatical subjects. In such a case, a tumour is felt just above the sternum, and this swelling has a tremulous motion like an aneurism. We may, however, very readily distinguish it from a disease of the artery. You must recollect, that when aneurism has gone so far as to protrude above the chest, the tumour from the coagulation of its contents, is almost incompressible. In varix, however, the motion is rather tremulous, and the swelling, even although large, is completely removed by pressure; its contents never coagulate, and its inner surface is never crusted over with lymphatic layers. It is therefore till the last, soft and compressible. Besides, when we have by pressure, completely emptied the cyst of its contents, if we remove the pressure, and desire the patient to cough, the tumour is instantly reproduced, and is rendered exceedingly tense; and at the same time, we can, in most cases, trace the turgescence up along the course of the jugular vein. Although, therefore, on a superficial view, varix of the termination of the jugular vein presents some of the features of arterial aneurism, yet you have seen that there are criteria, by attending to which, it would be inexcusable not to distinguish the one affection from the other.

In aneurism of the thoracic aorta, the practitioner has it not in his power to do more than merely palliate symptoms: With this view, the patient must be directed to use only the lightest, and at the same time, least nourishing food; to avoid fatigue, to keep the bowels open, to abstain from the use of wine or spirituous liquors, and to make use of digitalis. In internal aneurism, I can safely say, you will find no remedy more beneficial than digitalis. I do not however pretend to say, that it will cure the disease, neither would I wish you to believe, that in every case, it will even alleviate; on the contrary, I have known it used without producing any good effect; but I must be allowed to say, that I have never known it have a bad tendency.

WHERE there is a tendency to plethora, we may, along with the digitalis, occasionally detract a small quantity of blood, but we are not to push this evacuation to any great extent; for in most cases, it is not productive of the very beneficial effects we would expect to result from its employment. In some cases, it has even been supposed to accelerate death. You will find a case in the works of Morgagni, where the person died three hours after venesection. Bleeding is employed with most advantage, in those cases, where there is a great obstruction in breathing, and turgescence of the face; but except in such cases, we can, in general, by low diet, gain all that we could by bleeding; if we may credit Valsalva, we may actually starve the disease out of the system. This physician, with Hippocrates as his guide, set seriously to work to cure incipient aneurisms by starvation; and if the regimen enjoined by the Father of Physic was severe, the patients under the care of

Valsalva found the severity of the discipline in no degree relaxed. , This practitioner believed, that in this way he had cured an Italian Nobleman; and he was more firmly persuaded of this, when the patient some time afterwards died of another disease ; and when, on opening the body, he found the artery in the place where he supposed the aneurism to have been seated, reduced to its usual size, but in a manner callous.

I WOULD not have you believe, however, that in aneurism of any internal vessel, you have it in your power, even by the most rigid antiphlogistic regimen, to cure the complaint; but that regular diet, taken in sparing quantity, will mitigate the sufferings of the patient; is what I would most strenuously inculcate. In cases where the pain was very acute, some have found benefit from the tepid bath; and where the tumour has threatened to burst externally, Mr. A. Cooper of London has found, that this event may be retarded by supporting the integuments with sticking plaster. When however the disease has come this length, protracting life is only adding to the pain and anxiety produced by an incurable complaint.

REMARKS

CAUSES OF PRETERNATURAL PULSATION IN THE EPIGASTRIUM.

───────────────

Pulsating tumours are very frequently found about the epigastric region, and, in general, young practitioners, till undeceived by dissection, are apt to consider these as dependent on some organic affection, either of the heart or of the large vessels. When treating of chronic inflammation of the heart, and adhesion of the pericardium, I have mentioned, that in general, in the advanced stage of that disease, a beating is felt about the pit of the stomach. We have seen, when the pericardium is closely fixed to the heart, that this capsule is corrugated on every contraction of the ventricles; and, that thus, the diaphragm is raised along with the pericardium by which the liver is elevated. The ventricle having however completely emptied itself of its contents, again distends, and in proportion to the degree of dilatation, the liver and diaphragm descend, by which an impulse is communicated to the hand, when applied over the epigastrium. In some cases, this pulsation is more obscure than in others; and in some I have seen it so violent, that it even visibly affected the integuments. This is not however the only cause of apparent pulsation *in epigastrio;* neither is the pulsation in every case, produced by the impulse communicated to some solid tumour or substance interposed between the hand and the artery. In some cases, the beating is undoubtedly occasioned in this way, but in other instances, it is as certainly dependent on some nervous affection of the vessel itself.

ALTHOUGH it has long been known, even since the time of Hippocrates, that for a length of time, a patient may have pulsation in the epigastrium, without any disease of the heart, or aneurism of the large vessels, still no one, in so far as I know, has pointed out the various causes which give rise to this symptom. Morgagni, in his seventeenth letter, and twenty-eighth article, observes, that sometimes in dilatation of the heart, this organ descends so far, as to push the diaphragm before it into the hypochondrium, where the heart is felt beating; and may, from its effect on the stomach, be mistaken for an aneurism of the cœliac artery.

WHEN speaking of dilatation of the right side of the heart, complicated with malconformation of the mitral valve, I related the history of a case, where a most furious pulsation in the epigastric region, was produced entirely by the dilated heart. In this case, no one who saw the patient ever doubted, but that she had an aneurism of the cœliac artery; a supposition the more excusable, when we recollect, that on laying the hand along the chest, so as to embrace the lower part of the thorax and upper part of the abdomen, an apparent line of division was felt between the beating tumour at the pit of the stomach, and the heart. Besides, the action of the heart, and of the tumour, did not seem completely synchronous, from which it was inferred, that the pulsation *in epigastrio*, was caused by an affection of the large artery.

I MENTION these facts, to caution you against committing a similar mistake; for in general, when the heart is so much enlarged as to produce the pulsation *in epigastrio*, you will find this want of correspondence between the action of the heart and the tumour. If you recollect, that it is not the heart which you feel directly beating, but the liver, which, by the action of this organ is projected forward, you will at once understand, why there is a palpable difference in the time, when you perceive the stroke of the heart, and that of the tumour. I would also take occasion from this case to inform you, that where you are called to a patient in whom the pulsation is very perceptible, you may almost to a certainty decide, that it is not dependent on any organic disease of the arteries.

PRETERNATURAL pulsation about the epigastrium, may likewise be occasioned by incysted tumours, attached either to the lower surface of the diaphragm, or formed between the layers of the pericardium.   Of the latter species of disease, we have a history in the works of Lancisi, who relates, that on opening the subject, a large incysted tumour was found between the coats of the pericardium, where that capsule is attached to the diaphragm.

PULSATION is also often produced *in epigastrio,* by regurgitation of the blood along the vena cava inferior.   We have already seen some cases in which this had taken place; and I may now inform you, that the pulsation is occasionally rendered more distinct, by the vein being at the same time dilated.   There is a case of this kind in the work of Senac, where, from the vena cava being as large as the arm, the patient had a very violent pulsation in the epigastrium: a circumstance which you will understand, must generally in some degree or other happen, wherever the right auricle is preternaturally enlarged.   The influx of blood into the vessels of the liver, on the contraction of the auricle, must carry forward that viscus, produ-

cing an undulatory motion in the epigastrium ;
but every one who has felt this action, will
readily be able to distinguish it from aneurism.
It is both too diffused and undulatory for that
disease.

INCREASED solidity of the lungs, more especially of their lower acute margins, where they
overlap the pericardium, will also produce apparent pulsation about the scrobiculus cordis.
I saw a well marked case of this along with
Mr. Russel, some time ago. The patient was a
poor woman, much subject to hysteria, and especially tormented with cough, difficulty in
breathing, and beating about the pit of the
stomach. The pulsation was even at times so
violent, that it raised the integuments to a visible degree; and when the hand was laid over
the ensiform cartilage, the pulsation was dreadful; it was nearly as violent as in E. Brown,
who had the mitral valve malformed, and in
whom the right side of the heart was as large
as that of an ox. One who had never before
seen a case of anomalous pulsation, would, on
examining this patient, have had no doubt but
that either the trunk or some of the branches of
the cœliac artery were aneurismal. The difficulty of breathing, and working in the chest
increasing, put an end to her life. The body
was examined by Mr. Russel, Dr. Brown and
myself. We first inspected the heart, to get at
which, we were obliged to turn aside the lungs,

which were so solid, that although free from adhesion to the pleura, they did not collapse when the chest was opened; they remained perfectly erect, and on cutting through them, we found their parenchymatous substance greatly increased, and the bronchiæ so much compressed, that they contained very little air. The lungs had also descended lower than common, pushing before them the diaphragm, and their lobes were insinuated between the pericardium and the sternum. The pericardium was healthy, the heart was of its usual size, its valves were natural, and no disease could, by the most accurate investigation, be perceived in the vessels of either the thorax or abdomen.

It may be conceived from the history of this dissection, that no adequate cause was discovered for the pulsation *in epigastrio*, such, however, must suspend their judgment: Have we not seen, when the heart is dilated, and descends so low, as to affect the liver during its contraction and dilatation, that a pulsation sometimes very violent, is felt in the epigastric region? In this case, the lungs had lost their elasticity; they no longer had a free play in the thorax; they were so solid, that during the systole and diastole of the heart, they were, by the repercussions of this organ, made to communicate an impulse to the hand applied over the lower part of the chest. The pulsation in this woman was produced in precisely the same way, that it is where the heart descends so low as to affect the liver; only, I would observe, that in this case, the pulsation was more distressing than I have almost ever seen occur from a dilated heart. The patient, owing to the difficulty in breathing and beating at the pit of the stomach, was, for some weeks before her death, in a most deplorable condition. She was compelled to sit constantly erect, her cough was incessant, her breathing was gasping, and she durst scarcely, for fear of suffocation, venture to sleep. She presented a most miserable picture of disease; yet, notwithstanding the severity of her symptoms, she was not reduced in body.

INDURATION of the pancreas, scirrhus of the pylorus, or tumours at the root of the mesentery, in many patients, give rise to a suspicion of the existence of aneurism of either the aorta, or of the cœliac artery. A circumscribed tumour is felt in the place of this vessel, and the swelling is alternately raised and depressed by the action of the artery, with which it is in contact. The disease very much resembles aneurism; indeed, it is only in rare cases that we can determine the real nature of the complaint.

IT has already been said, that a tumour placed over the course of an artery, and attached to it, always pulsates more strongly than the vessel itself; and likewise that glandular swellings in the neck, are frequently mistaken for aneurism of the carotid artery. In the neck,

however, by handling the tumour, we can readily
ascertain its nature ; in the abdomen, our diagnosis can by no means be so certain, we cannot there grasp the swelling, we cannot feel
whether its own capacity is changed, or whether
it is merely moved by the action of the vessel
to which it adheres. In the other species of
pulsating tumours about the epigastrium, you
can by care determine whether they depend on
aneurism of any of the arteries; but in this affection, except from some of the concomitant
symptoms, you can have no guide. I have seen
several instances of this species of pulsating tumours, but in very few of them has the nature of
the case been determined while the patients
were alive.

ONE history, I may relate. It is that of a
woman above eighty years of age. During
the greater part of her life, she had been extremely healthy, but about three months before I saw her, which was at the request of
Mr. De Lys, she had been tormented with pain
about the pit of the stomach, and within the last
six weeks her attention had been particularly attracted to her complaint, by feeling a very
unpleasant pulsation *in epigastrio*. When I
examined her, a circumscribed pulsating tumour
was distinctly felt, just about the junction of
the epigastric, with the umbilical region. Its
action was synchronous with that of the arteries,
and it was excessively tender to the touch:

she complained of the whole belly being sore, when pressed on, and she could not easily lie on either side; the pulse was seventy, and of regular strength, her bowels were rather torpid, and she had occasional attacks of vertigo. This was the case when I saw the patient; and though from a review of the circumstances, I had no doubt that the tumour was not an aneurism, yet I could not pretend to determine on its real nature. In a few days she was examined by another surgeon more famous for the decision of his prognosis, than for the accuracy of his diagnosis, and he, judging from appearances, and laughing at those who questioned its being aneurism, asserted, that no man who knew what aneurism was, could doubt the nature of the tumour in the patient's belly. The patient was then examined by one or two other practitioners, who concurred in the supposition that it was not aneurism, but declined giving an opinion of its real nature, till one of them, from his displacing flatus from the tumour while he was pressing on it, conjectured that it was occasioned by a scirrhus pylorus, the rest wisely resolved to wait till death put it in their power to solve the difficulty by dissection.

THIS event happened in a few weeks, when it was ascertained, that the tumour was formed by a thickening of the pylorus, and scirrhus of the round head of the pancreas; and it was also clearly seen, that the pulsation had been occasioned by the influx of blood, into that portion of the aorta with which the tumour was connected. This part of the vessel was in a state of disease, its fibrous coats had lost their usual texture, and in many places thick scales of bone were deposited between them. The artery was for some inches incapable of re-acting on its contents. It had therefore ceased to be an artery; it was merely dilated by the influx of blood into it from the tract of the healthy artery above; and it produced the pulsation in the same way that the regurgitation of blood from an enlarged auricle along the cava inferior, occasions an undulatory motion of the liver. The nature of this case, from the absence of the usual symptoms which accompany scirrhus of the pylorus, would not, but for the accidental displacement of the flatus, have been detected before death. Indeed, from what has been stated, you will be convinced of the great difficulty there must be, in forming an accurate diagnosis in such a case; and therefore, it would perhaps be advisable, not to give a decided opinion on any case of this kind. This, if not the best, is at least the safest plan.

THE causes which have just been described, as giving rise to pulsation *in epigastrio,* are dependent as must have been observed, on the mechanical action of either the heart or arteries, or the neighbouring parts. Hippocrates, however, makes mention of a species of pulsation, evidently not produced in this way, and Morgagni relates one or two cases, in which the throbbing in the epigastrium was occasioned by some irregularity in the action of the abdominal vessels themselves.

THE disease in one case, began with prostration of strength, and unusual pulsation about the heart, conjoined with dyspnœa. These symptoms, for some time, continued to increase, and then the patient had a frequent tendency to syncope; violent fits of breathlessness, accompanied with intense pain in the right arm; but the most prominent feature in this man's complaint, was a violent and constant pulsation, reaching from the heart down to the umbilicus. The beating was so severe, that Morgagni says, he had seldom witnessed its equal: it was even visible externally, and the patient complained of similar pulsation all over the body. The carotid, temporal, and radial arteries were affected, " their pulsations " were large and vibrating." On the idea of the disease being an internal aneurism, he was more than once bled, but still the symptoms increasing in severity, he died on the fourth day after his admission into the hospital.

THE heart, abdominal viscera, and large vessels were all perfectly healthy, yet Morgagni conjectures, that this preternatural pulsation was occasioned by a state of the vascular system, similar to what predisposes to aneurism.

The essence of this in his estimation, consists in debility of the vessels, and increased strength of the heart; of this condition however, we have no proof, its existence is a gratuitous inference from improper data. It is more probable, as Morgagni himself afterwards observes, that this condition of the arterial system was dependent on nervous irritation. Cases in proof of this are to be found detailed in different parts of this author's letters; in the 9th number of the Edinburgh Medical and Surgical Journal, there is a very good paper on the subject of preternatural pulsation in the abdomen, by Dr. Albers of Bremen.

THIS writer, after detailing some very interesting cases of this preternatural pulsation, which I must inform you, do not all seem to have arisen from a nervous affection, concludes, " This pulsation may be best distinguished from " internal aneurism, with which it is apt to " be confounded, by the following symptoms. " Aneurism arises gradually, and the throbbing " therefore, also becomes by degrees stronger " and stronger; these pulsations on the con- " trary, occur suddenly, are generally strongest " at the first, and weaker when they have con- " tinued some time. In aneurism, the pulse " is usually synchronous with that at the wrist; " in these pulsations this is not always the case. " If the patient suffers under melancholy, hy- " pochondriasis, hysteria, or other nervous af-

" fections, if he has vomited blood, or dis-
" charges a blackish matter by stool; if disor-
" ganization of particular parts of the abdomen
" is discoverable by the touch, in all probabili-
" ty the pulsation is not caused by aneurism,
" although in describing it, Lieutaud has said,
" *melancholici, nulla sæpius prævia causa, in hunc*
" *dirum morbum sunt proclives.*"

As an illustration of this disease, which is not
of rare occurrence, I shall transcribe the history
of one of the patients recorded by Dr. Albers.
" A girl twenty-four years of age, who had al-
" most always enjoyed good health, one even-
" ing, while looking out at the window, fell
" back senseless on the floor. That morning
" her menses had appeared, and they continued
" to flow naturally during the whole period of
" her disease. So soon as she came to herself,
" she felt a desire to go to stool, and discharged
" a black pitchy matter, and again fainted.
" These symptoms continued during the whole
" night, and next morning; when I was called,
" I found her much debilitated, with her cheeks
" and lips pale, and scarcely able to whisper
" an answer to my questions; her respiration
" was laborious, pulse considerably small and
" quick, but somewhat hard; tongue clean,
" thirst great, and appetite entirely gone. I
" was also told by her parents, that for some
" days past, she had been constipated. In the
" evening my patient was in the same state,

" except that she had evacuated much of the
" black matter already mentioned, and had
" fainted at each discharge."

" NEXT morning, at five o'clock, I was sud-
" denly called to her, as she was believed to be
" dying. She was extremely exhausted, and the
" fainting fits succeeded each other almost
" without interruption ; she was only able to
" tell in low voice, that she felt a palpita-
" tion in her belly; when I laid my hand up-
" on it, I was in reality astonished at the vio-
" lent pulsation, which could be observed from
" the xyphoid cartilage, to below the navel,
" that is, almost to the place where the aorta
" divides into the two iliacs. When three fin-
" gers were laid across the pulsating body, the
" stroke could be felt by each of them. The
" pulsation of the heart was weaker than natu-
" ral ; the pulse at the hand extremely small,
" but not quicker than the preceding, and not
" synchronous with the pulsation in the abdo-
" men. I must confess, that at first, I took
" this pulsation for an aneurism, which was
" also the opinion of Mr Mayenhoff, an able
" surgeon. At noon, I requested Dr. Wien-
" halt to visit the patient, who immediately
" said, that he doubted if the pulsation pro-
" ceeded from an aneurism, because he remem-
" bered to have read some similar cases in
" Morgagni. At this time the pulsation was
" not half so strong as in the morning, and in-

" deed, never was so again. He advised me to
" go on with the evacuating remedies, and
" clysters already prescribed, but to combine
" some opium with the former. Under the use
" of these remedies, in a few days, the pulsa-
" tion and oppression at the breast were di-
" minished. The stools at first had the colour
" of boiled chocolate, and afterwards became
" natural. In general, the patient mended per-
" ceptibly, and in some weeks was perfectly
" recovered, although for six weeks, a weak
" pulsation could be felt in the abdomen; since
" that time, several years have elapsed, .and
" she has married and become the mother of
" a family, without any recurrence of these
" symptoms, but has on the whole been re-
" markably healthy."

AFTER this case, I do not consider it necessary to make any farther remarks on this affection, which, as Dr. Albers justly observes, very
often occurs in hysterical females, and hypo-
chondrical males, and in these patients is a
dreadful source of anxiety.

YOU thus learn, that pulsation *in epigastrio*
may be produced by adhesion of the heart to
the pericardium; by enlargement of the heart
itself, chiefly of the right side; by tumours attached to the diaphragm; by enlargement of
the vena cava inferior; by preternatural solidity
of the lungs; by any solid increase of substance
about the aorta, or roots of the large abdominal

arteries; and lastly, by a peculiar affection of the vascular system itself. You have also seen that sometimes this condition of the vascular system, is extended almost over the whole body, as in the case of the shoemaker, related by Morgagni; or is confined to the abdomen, as in the history I have extracted from Dr. Albers' essay. These are the different causes, which in so far as I know, give rise to preternatural pulsation *in epigastrio*, but I am far from wishing it to be believed, that they are the only sources from which this symptom may originate; neither would I have you consider the history of those which are noticed as perfect; the observations are more to be considered as an attempt to direct the attention to this subject, than as forming a complete history of these varied and anomalous affections.

REMARKS

UNUSUAL ORIGIN AND COURSE OF SOME OF THE LARGE AND IMPORTANT ARTERIES OF THE HUMAN BODY.

WHILE Anatomy was yet in its infancy, and Surgery was consequently rude and imperfect, much attention was bestowed on deviations from the natural distribution of the arterial system, and in some cases, an ideal importance was attached to their occurrence. Now, however, that indefatigable research has made us better acquainted with the structure of the human frame, our knowledge of the relative value of the different parts of which it is composed, has been progressively extended. Our ancestors, to whom we ought to be grateful for the information they have communicated to us, had, on the subject of Lusus in the vascular system, only vague and imperfect notions; nor could it

be otherwise, for where their real knowledge
failed them, they were abundantly willing to
make up the deficiency by conjecture; they
reasoned without any fixed principle to guide
them, and therefore, we cannot wonder that they
sometimes went wrong. By the experience we
have now derived from our extended knowledge
of Anatomy and Physiology, we are led to dis-
card many of their notions regarding the effects
resulting from unusual origin of different vessels; but still, although many of their opinions
be proved to be erroneous, yet we are indebted
to them for directing our attention to this enquiry, which is important. By tracing the deviations from the usual origin and course of the
large arteries, we shall be enabled to explain
many points in pathology, and circumstances
connected with the performance of operations,
which would otherwise remain in obscurity; and
it will likewise shew us how very contracted the
ideas of that anatomist must be, who supposes
that there is a regular standard for the origin
and distribution of the arteries in every subject.

A priori, a person would hardly suppose that
the aorta would ever be found to deviate from
its usual origin, yet in some cases, we find,
that in place of originating from the left ventricle, it takes its rise in part from the right,
and in part from the left. This fact is now incontrovertibly confirmed by repeated observation. When this malconformation takes place, a

most distressing disease results from the inter-
mixture of the pure and impure blood. In the
natural state of these parts, it is intended, that after birth, the two sides of the heart should act
perfectly independently of each other; it is provided that the right side should transmit its contents to the lungs, where the blood is to be pu-
rified, and then conducted by the pulmonary
veins to the left auricle. This is the scheme of
the perfect adult circulation, but its principle
is destroyed, where the aorta rises both from the
right and left ventricles. In this case, a part of
the impure blood of the pulmonic side of the
heart, is sent into the systemic circulation,
without passing through the lungs. The blood
of the arteries is only two thirds, or perhaps less,
arterial, it cannot properly support the vital functions; the body droops, and the person always
dark on the surface, becomes unable to exert
himself, is tormented with a short, stiffling, suffocating cough, feels cold in the extremities, and
after irregular intervals, is seized with paroxysms
of constriction in the chest, and difficulty in
breathing: his cough increases, his face becomes tumid and livid, his eyes are prominent,
he tosses about, and endeavours to force the
air, which has served its purpose, out of the
lungs; he therefore presses the chest against any
resisting object, which may happen to be near.
He is apparently in great agony, and is convulsed; yet, even when he is struggling most, at the

moment when he seems on the eve of parting with life, he is in reality performing the only act which can prolong it. He is expelling the contaminated air, and at each gasp, is introducing a quantity of purer air; this is repeated, till at last the blood is so far rendered arterial, that the functions are restored to their usual languid state. This mode of circulation is radically bad; in the very young child, it does not absolutely destroy life, but when farther advanced, it is every hour in imminent danger of sudden suffocation, and seldom reaches manhood. A knowledge of the consequences of this lusus, teaches us that we have it not in our power to obviate the bad effects of such a construction of the vascular system. All we can do is, to palliate the severity of the most prominent symptoms, by enjoining rest and a rigid abstinence from stimuli, and perhaps also by advising the patient to inhale oxygen gas. When these have been tried, every thing has been done which art can do, and how little this is, must be learned from the review of the cases on record.

IN general, the arteria anonyma is the first trunk that originates from the arch of the aorta. Sometimes however, the right subclavian and carotid arteries take their origin separately from this vessel; the right carotid being the trunk first sent off, and the subclavian the last. A case of this lusus is recorded by Dr. Monro, jun. in his thesis. In this subject; the sub-

clavian artery besides being unusual in its origin, was also uncommon in its course. It took
its rise from that part of the aorta where the
vessel was about to become descending aorta,
and in place of running upwards along the front
of the aspera arteria, it insinuated itself between it and the œsophagus; and by passing in
a slanting direction between them, it reached
the right side of the trachea, where it as usual
began to give off its branches to the neighbouring parts.

THIS species of lusus is very rarely seen, and
if it be always productive of the same consequences which accompanied it in this patient,
it is very fortunate that it so seldom occurs.
In this instance, a very alarming, and in the
end, a fatal degree of dysphagia was produced,
though it be somewhat difficult to conceive,
how this event was connected with its supposed
cause. If dysphagia be really produced by this
unusual course of the artery, I need hardly add,
that the disease must be incurable; nay, that it
will scarcely admit even of palliation. If we
attempt to alleviate, it must be by the employment of such measures as abate over-action in
the vascular system.

SOMETIMES when the arteria anonyma arises
from its proper spot, we find that it follows an
improper course. Commonly when the arteria
innominata has got to a level with the top of
the sternum, it has reached the right side of the

trachea, where it divides into its two trunks.
In some subjects however, it rises much higher along the front of the windpipe; in several
I have found it touching the lower border of
the thyroid gland. This variation in the position of the artery, ought always to be recollected in performing the operation of tracheotomy.
In a person in whom the artery runs in this
way, which cannot readily be ascertained *a
priori*, were we in operating, to use the knife
rashly in the last stage of the dissection, we
might perhaps wound this vessel. If we only
divide the integuments and the fasciæ with
the scalpel, and then employ the finger to clear
the trachea, this accident can never happen.
When we have fairly brought the windpipe into
view with the finger, then we must depress this
vessel, and with the scalpel, cut the rings of
the trachea from below upward. This mode of
operating I would prefer, if my intention were
to perform tracheotomy, but I do not pretend
to say, that this operation ought to be had recourse to as preferable to laryngotomy. However, if the Surgeon has determined on tracheotomy, it may be proper to state, that this operation may, with care, be as safely performed on
a very young, as on a full grown subject. In the
early part of life, from the non-evolution of the
larynx, there is fully as large a space between
the lower margin of the thyroid gland, and
the top of the sternum, as at any after period. It

is also worthy of being known and remembered, that in the adult, by bending back the head, we gain in measurement, chiefly above the thyroid gland; but in infancy, by the same means, we gain most in the space between the gland and the sternum.

IN those cases, where both carotid arteries originate from the arteria anonyma, there must be some risk in performing the operation of tracheotomy; for in such cases, the left carotid crosses the front of the windpipe pretty high in the neck. Professor Scarpa has seen a specimen of this distribution in a male subject, and I have met with three.

IN performing the operation of tracheotomy we may injure the right carotid artery, but this is most likely to happen, in those people in whom the arteria innominata rises considerably to the left side of the trachea. I am in possession of a cast taken from a boy of twelve years of age, which shews the right carotid artery crossing the trachea in an oblique direction. In this subject, this vessel did not reach the lateral part of the trachea, till it had ascended two inches and a quarter above the top of the sternum.

THE common carotid artery ascends in general a single and undivided vessel, till it reaches the top of the thyroid cartilage. About this spot it divides into its large external and internal trunks. We cannot however say, that it bifurcates at the angle of the jaw; this is a most uncertain rule, for the position of the angle of the jaw, varies according to the period of life at which we examine the subject. It is relatively high seated previous to the evolution of the teeth; and therefore in infancy the large arteries are much exposed. This exposure continues till the evolution of the permanent teeth has brought the jaw to its just proportion with the other parts of the body. In the adult we therefore generally find the bifurcation of the carotid placed near to the angle of the jaw, but this never happens in the young subject, neither is it uniformly met with even in the full grown person. The place of division of the common carotid artery, is liable to great variety both in point of situation and appearance, sometimes it bifurcates low in the neck, at other times, it does not divide at all, but merely sends off branches on every side, and in not a few instances, instead of the external carotid artery, we find a series of large branches. In one of our subjects, the common carotid separated into its two trunks low in the neck, opposite to the upper edge of the sixth cervical vertebræ. The trunks which were nearly of equal size, mounted up the side of the larynx parallel to each other, and were inveloped as usual in the same sheath with the internal jugular vein, and eight pair of nerves. The place of division of the carotid, was three inches below the angle of the jaw. It has been assumed as an axiom, by one writer after another, that in the neck, no large artery except the common carotid is met with, till we ascend near to the angle of the jaw. Although this be in general correct, still it is not prudent in the operator to depend too much on its universality; neither is it advisable for the anatomist dogmatically to assert, that only a single artery lies in a certain space of the neck. I have had thrice occasion to see two large vessels very low in the neck, and in these cases they were only separated from each other by interposed cellular membrane; and had a Surgeon been called on to perform an operation in the vicinity of these vessels, he would naturally have been on his guard till he had secured one of the trunks; when he had done this, he might perhaps have imagined, that now that the carotid was out of the way, he had little to dread: the very next stroke of his knife would have convinced him that security was only to be found in knowledge. This would have satisfied him, that an accurate acquaintance with the usual deviations from the natural situation of the large arteries was of high value, not indeed as many imagine, for the purpose of gratifying unmeaning curiosity, but for a nobler end, to prepare himself to meet the dangers and difficulties which occur in practice.

IN some subjects the common carotid does not divide into the external and internal trunks, but the primary branches of the external carotid all strike off at one spot from the side of the great vessel. In a preparation of the vessels of the head and neck, which is in my possession, the external carotid is a short thick stump, resembling the axis arteriæ cœliacæ, and like it, from the top of this the large branches take their rise. This mode of arrangement of the branches constitutes a very beautiful species of lusus; for as the parts on which the vessels are to be distributed lie above, and on every side, the branches in their course to these form a fine vascular fan.

IN another preparation which is in our possession, the common carotid, instead of dividing in the neck, sends off lateral branches till it reaches considerably beyond the angle of the jaw. When the artery comes opposite to the root of the styloid process, it divides into two vessels, one the internal carotid, the other the conjoined trunk of the temporal and maxillary arteries.

In operating about the neck, it is necessary to be aware of these varieties in the arrangement of the vessels about the angle of the jaw. In some operations, it is necessary to include the external carotid in a ligature. Were a surgeon to attempt to do this in a person in whom all the primary vessels of the carotid branched off from a common origin, he would be considerably puzzled how to act. In the case where the common carotid gives off all the branches, except the internal maxillary and temporal arteries, before it divides, he would be no less embarrassed. It is much easier to take up the external, than to include the common carotid in a ligature; the former lies anteriorly, and on the tracheal side of the latter; consequently, it is considerably removed from the large nerves. These are indeed in absolute contact with the common carotid, and attached to it by cellular membrane; so likewise is the internal jugular vein. In our operations, we would therefore wish to avoid any interference with this artery, as, without great care, and much delicacy of dissection, we could hardly take it up, without injuring either the vein or nerves. It is even on the dead body, a difficult matter to separate the nerves and vessels from each other. How much more difficult it must be to do so in the living, where all the parts are covered with blood, and the person struggling from pain, can only be understood by those who have been in the habit of seeing operations performed.

THE upper thyroid is liable to very great uncertainty in its origin; sometimes it comes off from the very spot where the carotid separates into its two trunks, at other times it arises low in the neck, from the common carotid, and it is often the first branch of the external carotid. In one of our subjects, the lingual and upper thyroid arteries originated by a common trunk, from the external carotid. In another, the lingual and facial artery arose together. In a vascular bust, which was given me by Dr. Brown, there is a complete transposition of the external and internal maxillary arteries. In this, the facial artery takes its origin from the temporal artery, nearly about the angle of the jaw. Besides, at the precise spot of the external carotid from which the facial ought to have come off, a vessel originates, which soon sends off the submental artery, and then rises upward, behind the ascending plate of the lower jaw, supplying the place of the internal maxillary artery.

IN two or three subjects I have seen the labial artery as small as a sewing thread where it passed over the jaw, and in those instances it did not reach higher than the lower lip. The place of the vessel was supplied by the arteria transversalis faciei, which was larger than a crow quill, and distributed precisely on the same parts which ought to have received branches from the labial artery.

THESE varieties in the origin and course of the primary branches of the external carotid artery are neither frequent nor important; they are never taken into account in operating; yet the Surgeon ought to know that such varieties do exist.

IF the branches of the carotid artery be liable to variety in their origin and distribu-

tion, those of the subclavian are no less so.
I could from my own specimens enumerate
a great diversity, but as few of the branches
arising from the subclavian artery are regular,
I shall only notice the most important deviations from the usual course of these vessels. The
inferior artery of the thyroid gland is very uncertain in regard to its origin, course, and size;
sometimes it is as large as a goose quill, at
other times it is hardly perceptible, and in some
subjects it is altogether wanting. It generally
lies behind the common carotid artery, and is
distributed chiefly on the back and lower part
of the gland: in some rare instances however,
it has been found running on the front of the
carotid artery; and in one preparation, in the
possession of Dr. Barclay, the two lower thyroid
arteries rise by a common trunk from the right
of the subclavian. In this specimen the course
of the vessel is also unnatural, for in place
of grasping the inferior and posterior part of
the gland, it creeps up the side of the trachea,
lower than the gland; and when it has reached
the front of the windpipe, it divides into two
branches, the right runs along the trachea, and
the left ascends within two tracheal rings of the
cricoid cartilage. The first lies, as I have been
informed, nearly in the line of the small vein
which generally covers the trachea, and which,
in the operation of tracheotomy is usually divided; the artery therefore, must be equally

liable to injury as the vein. One objection brought against tracheotomy is, the trouble arising from the passage of the blood into the windpipe; where however the lower thyroid artery runs in its proper course, and where the descending vein is not larger than usual, this objection is of no moment. Even where the artery does lie in such a position as to be unavoidably cut, still by the tenaculum, we may prevent any hæmorrhage into the trachea.

IN a few instances, the vertebral artery, instead of originating from the subclavian vessel, comes off as an independent trunk from the arch of the aorta. This is the case in a vascular bust which was prepared by Dr. Brown while in London; neither in this, nor in some other similar preparations which I have seen, has the artery been larger than natural. From the depth of the vessel and its course, it can seldom, if ever, come in the way of injury during operation.

THE thoracic axillary vessels are so extremely irregular, both in their origin and course, that it is altogether impossible to fix on any standard. We seldom see these vessels similar in their origin and distribution in two subjects; and we still more rarely meet with them of the same size in different bodies. It is however worthy of notice, that although the point of the axillary vessel whence the thoracic arteries arise be extremely unsettled, yet the subsequent distribution of these vessels is pretty regular. Thus, although we often find the long thoracic artery originating from different parts of the axillary artery, or even in some instances observe it coming off from one of the other thoracic vessels, still it almost invariably runs toward the side of the chest, between the greater and smaller pectoral muscles: the same holds true respecting the other arteries found in the axilla; the origin, therefore, is of less consequence than the course of these arteries, which ought to be classed under two divisions. If the Surgeon in studying the anatomy of the arm-pit recollect, that the largest of the arterial branches in that cavity attach themselves to the pectoral muscles on the forepart, and to the teres major, and latissimus dorsi behind, he will at once perceive, that in the usual distribution of these arteries, there can be no danger of wounding them in the extirpation of enlarged glands. A glandular tumour, unless very large, is never connected with more than its own nutrient artery. In most cases, therefore, where any of the large vessels about the axilla have been injured, the fault has been more on the part of the operator than of the disease. I will venture to say, that except in a very few cases where from other circumstances an operation is out of the question, the morbid connections are rarely such, as to render it necessary to injure any of the important vessels.

I HAVE however known several cases, wherein not only the thoracic arteries were cut, but

even some in which the great vein did not escape. A poor man was admitted into a public hospital on account of a diseased mamma,
accompanied with enlargement of the axillary
glands, and it was judged proper to remove both
the breast and glands by operation. The Surgeon, digging deep into the axilla, had nearly
excavated this cavity, when emboldened by
his success, and ignorant of the danger, he
made a full sweep with the knife, and fairly
cut across the axillary vein. He started back
in terror when he saw the blood gush from the
axilla, but soon recollected himself so far as to
thrust a sponge into the wound. An assistant
endeavoured by powerful pressure with the
thumbs, both above and below the clavicle, to
stop the hæmorrhage; but the blood still continued to flow by the side of the wadding which
had been thrust into the wound, and the patient fainted. The surgeon and assistants now
for the first time, discovered that it was a venous hæmorrhage, and then they did what
they ought to have done long before, they pressed on the vein below where it was cut, and thus
suppressed the bleeding, till they had tied the
vessel. The man died next day. Presence of
mind, and an accurate knowledge of the healthy
structure of the arm-pit, are the Surgeon's only
security in the extirpation of diseased glands
from that cavity.

IN an old woman, I found the humeral artery bound down by a slip of tendon, which arose from the latissimus dorsi muscle, and after crossing the large artery, was implanted into the bone along with the tendon of the pectorales major muscle: when this construction was brought into view, it occurred to us, that from the position of the slip, the humeral artery must have had the current of blood impeded, during the action of the latissimus dorsi muscle. As we knew the subject, we made the necessary inquiries, and found that she had really been less able to exert that arm than the other. It was, however, chiefly during these motions, which required that the latissimus dorsi muscle should be called into action, that she complained of weakness in the arm. Her friends specified, that she had never been able to beat a carpet, or pump a well with ease.

THE humeral artery is subject to a lusus, which is rarely met with in the lower extremity. We very frequently find the brachial artery dividing into the radial and ulnar vessels high in the arm. As a proof of the slight attention which had been paid to the vascular system, it may be worth observing, that even the illustrious Haller was ignorant of the existence of this distribution; Sharp is among the first who has described this lusus, and he considers it as of rare occurrence. But now that dissection is more practised than it formerly was, we have become well acquainted with the de-

viations from the usual course of the vessels of
the superior extremity, and from observation,
we are led to view these as very common. We
oftener meet with a high origin of the radial,
than of the ulnar artery; but when the latter
vessel comes off high, it is in general nearer
the axilla, than when the radial vessel is the
unnatural branch. The radial artery seldom
comes off higher than the fold of the pectoral muscle, but often much lower, and in all
the specimens of this lusus in our possession,
we have found both the radial, and ulnar arteries covered by the fascia. As I have now examined above twenty such cases, and have invariably found the vessels below the fascia, I
have less hesitation than I would otherwise have,
in supposing that Mr. Bell's description of this
lusus, is incorrect.

WHEN this deviation from the common distribution of the humeral arteries was discovered,
the operators of the day, considered such an occurrence as their only hope of saving the limb after the operation for aneurism. They ascribed to
these lusus, what we now attribute to the agency of vascular inosculation; they founded their
prospects of success on a comparatively rare arrangement of vessels; we, on the other hand,
proceed boldly to the operation, knowing that
the anastomosis of the small branches, is fully
competent to support the member. They, from
their ignorance of the vascular system, and want

of experience of the resources of the frame, performed the operation for aneurism with fear and trembling, and instead of expecting a favourable and uniform result, they rather wondered how the cure was effected; and in place of investigating the laws which regulate the vascular actions, they mispent their time in frivolous speculations about supernumerary vessels, and idle conjectures regarding their influence in saving the limb.

SINCE Mr. Bell's works have been published, the value of these high divisions of the artery has been much depreciated; indeed they are now seldom mentioned, except as matters of curiosity. If, however, it be remembered, that the radial artery when it comes off high, is uniformly covered, as well as the ulnar vessel, with the fascia; and if it be stated, that almost invariably, when the ulnar artery originates high, it descends above the fascia; we shall be enabled to explain some phenomena which are sometimes seen when the brachial vessels are wounded. The fact of both vessels lying beneath the fascia, when the radial artery rises high, and the ulnar, when it comes off high, running more superficial than the fascia, are points highly necessary to be kept in recollection.

THIS knowledge teaches the Surgeon, that the artery may be injured in two situations at the bend of the arm; it may be wounded either more superficial, or deeper seated than the fascia. If the radial artery be hurt, the tumour formed by the effused blood, from being placed beneath the fascia, will be firm and tense; the fore arm will be half bent; the member will be cold and benumbed; at the elbow joint, the swelling by the pressure of the biceps aponeurosis, will be divided into two portions; the one nearest the internal condyle of the humerus, from the weakness of the fascia at that part, will be the most prominent. When, however, the ulnar artery is wounded, the blood is poured out into the meshes of the subcutaneous cellular membrane; the limb is immediately swelled to a great size, is livid, and feels even colder than in the former instance. Mr. Bell, in his book on the arteries, when speaking about wounds of the humeral artery, observes, that sometimes when this vessel is injured, the effused blood protrudes forward the wounded artery, which is felt beating on the front of the tumour. This statement, I must confess, is to me quite unintelligible. I cannot understand how the trunk of the humeral artery can be projected on the forepart of the swelling. This vessel is firmly bound to the brachialis and triceps muscle, by the ramus anastomoticus, and the arteria profunda externa; till these, therefore, be torn across, the large artery cannot be pushed forward; it will, I believe, puzzle Mr. Bell, to explain how these vessels can be lacerated.   The explanation of this fact I suspect, must be sought for in the high origin of the ulnar artery.   We know, that when this vessel rises high, it lies above the fascia ; if, therefore, in such a person the radial artery be hurt, as the blood is poured out behind the fascia, the ulnar artery will be found pulsating on the front of the tumour, immediately beneath the skin. This I imagine has misled others besides Mr. Bell.

GENERALLY, when the ulnar artery rises high, it gives off the ramus anastomoticus major, which perforates the fascia, to reach the back part of the internal condyle of the humerus. In these cases, invariably both ulnar recurrent arteries have had their place supplied by branches from the artery, which follows the course of the interosseous vessel, and which, when the ulnar runs subcutaneous, is preternaturally large. When the radial artery originates high in the arm, it usually runs to the hand before it anastomoses with the ulnar vessel; but in some cases, I have seen it receive a trifling addition from this vessel at the bend of the elbow. Where the radial artery is small, the place of the radial recurrent is supplied by a branch from the other vessel.

IN three instances, where the radial artery came off high, I have found a projection of bone standing out from the front of the humerus, where it is covered by the fibres of the brachialis muscle. I have often met with a high division of the humeral artery, without these processes being present, but have never seen the latter without finding at the same time a premature division of the artery.

I HAVE met with three cases of lusus in the course of the ulnar artery. In three subjects, who were females, the humeral artery did not divide till it came near to the bend of the arm: As soon as it had divided, the ulnar artery, instead of passing beneath the flexor muscles of the carpus, it perforated the fascia, and attached itself to the basilic vein, along which it descended towards the wrist. In this, and the former lusus of the ulnar artery, from the vessel being absolutely in contact with the subcutaneous veins, there would have been considerable risk of its being injured, if a careless practitioner had attempted to bleed in the vein which lies over it: If, however, a person be at all attentive, this accident may be prevented ; for as the artery lies above the fascia, it is readily felt beating more superficially than usual, and may therefore easily be avoided. In those cases which we have seen, the pulsation has been nearer the internal condyle than usual, but this is not uniform.

VASA abberrantia, or branches running from one part of the artery to another, are frequently met with in the arm. In this species of lusus, a branch often rises about the insertion of the deltoid muscle, is seldom larger than a crow quill, and is generally lost about the bend of the arm. I have seen five of these lusus, and among them two varieties have been observable. The first was, where the vas aberrans, gave off the ramus anastomoticus major, previous to its joining with the radial artery, which made a sweep upward to receive it. The second was, that in which the ramus anastomoticus major rose from the humeral artery, and the vas aberrans merely gave off small muscular twigs in its course. All the vasa aberrantia which I have seen, have run parallel to the great artery, in contact with it, and covered by the fascia.

IN some subjects, the radial artery, very soon after its origin, gives off the arteria superficialis volæ, which is long, small, and in some cases tortuous, and descends in the situation of the radial artery, which twists to the back of the radius. In this lusus, of which we have seen several examples, and of which Dr. Baird has observed three instances in the same family, mistakes may arise with regard to the state of the patient. In a patient whose arm is in my possession, such a blunder was made by the attendant physician, who was a keen Brunonian. The patient, when he first consulted his physician, had a greater number of imaginary, than of real complaints. The practitioner, as it behoved him, felt at the wrist for his pulse, which from the peculiar arrangement of the arteries, was weak and tremulous. Bark and wine were necessarily prescribed, and for the sake of the latter, the patient was in no haste to recover. At last, he was taken ill in good earnest, and died. On dissecting him, we found that the physician had never felt the pulsation of the radial artery, having all along mistaken the action of the arteria superficialis volæ, for that of the radial. In fever, a blunder of this kind in the hands of a Brunonian, might be attended with serious consequences. When, therefore, other symptoms would lead us to form a different judgment respecting the case, we are not to trust to the state of the pulse at the wrist, but before we estimate the danger, or decide on the nature of the affection, we are to examine the state of the vascular action in some other part of the body.

THE arteria superficialis volæ, is exceedingly liable to variations in size in different subjects. In some, it is as small as a sewing thread, in which case, it seldom reaches farther than the ball of the thumb, but in others, it is of a very large size. I have frequently seen it considerably larger than a crow quill, and in some instances, it even surpasses the posterior branch of the radial artery. When the volar artery is preternaturally large, it passes into the palm of the hand, where it anastomoses freely with the palmer division of the ulnar artery. The two vessels joining, form a large vascular arch in the palm of the hand.

FROM the locality of the superficial volar artery it is much exposed to casual injury ; and if I may judge from what I have myself observed, in one or two cases, wounds of this vessel are as difficult to manage, as those of the radial artery. Some Surgeons have mistaken the one for the other. When the volar artery is wounded by the knife slipping, as in cutting stale bread, or hard cheese, the cut is generally made just at that point where the vessel touches the distal extremity of the radius; and as at this spot the artery is imbedded among a considerable quantity of cellular matter, it in part confines the blood, which is injected into the meshes of the cellular membrane, for some space round the wound. Wherever this has taken place, all regular character of the wounded artery is destroyed: The blood does not now issue from a regular and defined orifice, such as would be formed by a simple division of the large volar artery, but it oozes from innumerable pores like water from a sponge.

AN intelligent Surgeon will never be deceived by this, and he will be the more on his guard, if he has had an opportunity of perusing Mr. John Bell's very interesting description of wounds of the radial artery. He will not, as some practitioners have done, first tie one cell, then pull off the ligature and tie another, and thus go on groping about the wound, and teazing the patient till he becomes faintish, when the bleeding ceases, and the Surgeon rejoices that at last he has secured the vessel.

ONE who trusts to this treatment, must not be surprised although called on soon after, to stop the bleeding, which has again broken out with more fury than before. With these messages he must lay his account, so long as he persists in this plan of treatment. Let him therefore boldly decide upon, and promptly put in execution the securing of the artery, not at the wounded spot, but at some distance above it. Before doing so, however, it will be advisable that he ascertain, whether it be a preternaturally large volar artery which has been wounded, or whether it be the radial artery itself. If it be the volar artery, he will feel the pulsation of the posterior branch of the radial, at the root of the metacarpel bone of the thumb, but if the trunk of the radial artery be cut this pulsation will be wanting. Where the volar artery only is injured, it is not necessary to tie the trunk of the radial: we are, on the contrary, to continue the incision upwards from the wound, cutting through the placenta-looking mass till we reach the artery.

In one case which came under my own observation, the sound artery was secured, at the distance of about half an inch above the original wound. When we have fairly exposed the volar artery, we are before passing the ligature round it, to separate the nerve from the vessel with the nail of the finger, and then, with a blunt pointed curved needle, •we are to slip the thread under the artery. Some Surgeons have considered it indispensably necessary, that a surgical needle should be employed in doing this; nothing however is more certain, than that a simple contrivance may in cases of urgency be substituted for this instrument; we can very readily employ a common sewing needle for this purpose. Before attempting to bend this kind of needle, it must be made red hot, either by holding it in the fire, or in the flame of a candle, and allowed to cool slowly : after this, it may readily be curved to any extent, and it may then, as occasion requires, be employed either as a sharp or a blunt needle. If it is to be used as the latter, the eye part of the needle is to be used as the point.

Some may perhaps ridicule the mentioning this, which is so simple, as to be self-evident; but it is to be recollected, that a young practitioner seldom ventures to deviate from what he has read in his books, or heard at lecture. To him, therefore, even a simple hint may be of advantage; and I think I could instance one or two cases, in which such a hint would have been advantageous even to old practitioners. For example, a Surgeon was called to a man who lay weltering in blood, and almost in the agonies of death, from a wound of the femoral artery. This practitioner having heard that a tourniquet was useful in stopping hæmorrhage, and not happening to have one in his pocket, never looked at the patient, but turned about his horse and set off at full gallop for the necessary instrument, which he was to procure at the distance of four miles from where the man was. Before he had rode a quarter of a mile, he was overtaken by a messenger sent to inform him that the person was actually dead. I shall not take it upon me to say that this patient's life would have been saved even by the tourniquet; but every surgeon must, or should know, that a handkerchief firmly twisted about the thigh, will supply sufficiently well the place of a tourniquet.

THE anterior interosseous artery is not unfrequently peculiar in its distribution. In common, this vessel very soon after its origin from the ulnar artery, divides into two branches; the superficial is the smaller of the two, and is lost in the substance of the flexor sublimus digitorum, and long flexor of the thumb. The deep seated, attaches itself to the interosseous ligament, along which it descends, giving off twigs on every side. It is still a large vessel when it reaches the upper margin of the pronator quadratus, where it perforates the ligament, becoming a posterior vessel. Sometimes however, the case is reversed; the deep seated branch is very small, and almost exhausted before it reaches the quadratus muscle, but the superficial is as large as the radial or ulnar artery, and passes down between the flexor sublimus digitorum, and the flexor carpi radialis muscles. When the vessel still undiminished in size, reaches the annular ligament, it passes along with the flexor tendons beneath the ligament. It then enters the palm of the hand, where it sometimes sends a branch of communication to the ulnar artery, but oftener it continues a separate trunk, which is distributed on the ulnar side of the thumb, both sides of the forefinger, and on the radial side of the mid-finger. This artery just above the wrist, is as superficial as the radial artery, it may like that vessel, be accidentally wounded, and that it is this unusual vessel which has been hurt, we may infer from the wound being midway between the radial and ulnar arteries. In searching for this vessel, we are to cut through the fascia, and separate the palmaris longus, and flexor sublimus from the flexor carpi radialis; whereas when we are in quest of the radial artery, we must separate the flexor carpi radialis from the supinator radii longus muscle.

THE bronchial and abdominal arteries are extremely liable to variations, both in their origin and distribution, but as these have no reference to surgical practice it is not necessary to specify them.

THE pudic artery in some subjects, instead of passing out of the pelvis between the sacro-

sciatic ligaments, attaches itself to the lateral
and inferior part of the bladder, and traverses
the upper segment of the prostate gland in its
course to the ramus of the ischium.   I have
dissected four bodies with this lusus, and it is
proper to notice, that all of the subjects have
been males.   In the female, we can see an obvious reason for the pudic artery passing behind
the spine of the ischium, but in the male it will
be difficult to discover any satisfactory cause
for the existence of the same arrangement.   We
may indeed conjecture, like Mr. Hunter, that
nature wished to form the corresponding parts
in similar animals, as nearly alike as would be
consistent with the difference of function.   Were
the pudic artery to run on the inside of the
sacro-sciatic ligament in the female, it might
be very severely injured during the passage
of the head of the child.   In the other sex however, this can be no cause for the protection
of the vessel, and accordingly we sometimes
find it deviating in males from its usual course.
In all the instances of this lusus which have
come to my knowledge, the artery has run
above that portion of the prostate gland which
projects beyond the side of the urethra.   In the
common operation for the removal of calculi
from the bladder, if the gorget happen to cut
the pudic artery, as the vessel lies attached to
the solid bone, we have it in our power to repress
the hæmorrhage by the introduction of a piece
of sponge wrapped round a canula.

In operating on a person with this lusus, in the mode recommended by Dr. Thomson, we must invariably divide the pudic artery, which at the place of division, is too deeply seated to admit of being secured by ligature, and is so loosely connected with the neighbouring parts, and so remote from the bone, that pressure with the sponge can have no effect in preventing the loss of blood. I know from frequent experiment, that the plan of operating advised by Dr. Thomson, is easily executed, and were it not for the risk of this lusus, is fully as expedient as any in use. For my own part, from this circumstance, I would be inclined to divide the lateral, instead of the upper part of the prostate gland, but I would never employ the gorget to do this, neither would I ever use the knife as a gorget. If in cutting the side of the prostate gland, we injure the pudic artery, we know from experience, that we have it in our power either to secure the artery by ligature, or if this be impracticable, we can stop the hæmorrhage by the sponge. There are however, various contrivances for guarding the pudic artery from injury. I have sometimes on the dead subject, employed the plan described in a sketch of the operation of lithotomy, inserted in the Edinburgh Medical and Surgical Journal, and sometimes I still farther simplify this mode. In some subjects, I have lately, after exposing the prostate gland, and introducing a straight staff into the bladder, through an opening made into the membranous part of the urethra, insinuated a slip of pasteboard between the prostate and the tuberosity of the ischium. This affords a complete defence to the pudic artery, while I slit open the side of the prostate gland with a narrow bladed scalpel, conducted along the straight staff. In cutting the prostate, the knife is to be employed as a knife, and in no measure as a gorget. The scalpel is first to be conducted into the bladder, and then the staff is to be pressed to the right tuber, while we cut outward toward the left, dividing thus, all that portion of the prostate which is between the knife and the pasteboard. We are thus secured from injuring the pudic artery, and are rendered independent of the staff during the most hazardous part of the operation.

THE obturator artery is generally esteemed a branch belonging to the internal iliac vessel, but in reality, we might almost with equal propriety consider it as derived from the external iliac artery, or from one of its branches. It is often found rising, from the external iliac artery, about an inch above Paupart's ligament, in this case it bends over the brim of the pelvis in close contact with the bone, and from its commencement, to where it reaches the obturator hole, is in no risk of being concerned in the performance of any surgical operation. The obturator and epigastric arteries, likewise very frequently come off together. When the obturator and epigastric vessels separate from each other, very soon after they have come off from the iliac vessel, the obturator artery, if crural hernia take place into the lymphatic sheath, will in general be pushed to the ilial side of the neck of the sac, but if the obturator and epigastric vessels run on a considerable way before they separate, then almost invariably, if crural hernia take place into the lymphatic sheath, the obturator artery will encircle the neck of the sac. Many have supposed, that where the obturator comes off from the epigastric by the short origin, the vessel must invariably in crural hernia be turned to the ilial side of the sac. This is perfectly correct, provided the tumour be lodged in the sheath of the lymphatics; but if the hernia be placed in the sheath of the vein, the artery, even although it arise by the short origin, may surround the neck of the sac. These varieties in the locality of the obturator artery in crural hernia will be best understood, by reviewing the anatomy of the common and proper sheaths of the blood vessels.

THE internal orifice of the common sheath of the femoral vessels is placed just at the inner edge of Paupart's ligament. This opening is consequently wide, and of a triangular shape, containing nearest to the ilium, the great artery, then a septum stretched from the sharp edge of the crural arch, to the psoas aponeurosis, then on the pubal side of this curtain, the great vein is seated, and on the pubal side of it, the crural foramen is placed. This allows

transmission in every case to a set of lymphatics, and is sometimes occupied by a gland.
This is generally believed to be the anatomy of
the vascular sheath, but whoever carefully ex-
amines this, will be at once convinced, that besides the common sheath, the artery and vein
have each a separate and distinct sheath.   It is
not material to ascertain the precise point from
which these proper sheaths arise; perhaps they
may be of the same nature with the cellular
sheath investing the vessels in other parts, this
is however a matter of no consequence.   In
studying the nature of the parts concerned in
crural hernia, the only importance of these
sheaths, is derived from their mode of attachment to the sharp edge of Paupart's ligament.
If the artery and vein be cut across about half
an inch above the crural arch, the vessels re-
treat within their proper sheaths, which are
seen firmly united to the internal margin of
Paupart's ligament, and at the spot where the
sheaths are divided, they are observed by their
junction, forming a septum between the artery
and the vein.

By examining more narrowly, it will be ascertained that the lymphatics have no proper
sheath, for they lie covered only by that portion
of the common sheath, placed nearer to the pubis than the great vein; the orifice therefore,
leading into that part of the common sheath
appropriated to the lymphatics, is seated at the
inner edge of Paupart's ligament, but at this

part, no opening naturally leads into the proper or common sheath of either the artery or vein. In most cases, a thin layer from the transversalis fascia, is stretched over the mouth of the lymphatic sheath, in some subjects this is wanting, in which case, the orifice of the sheath forms the crural foramen. Till I saw the proper sheaths of the artery and vein, and had ascertained their mode of junction with the ligament of Paupart, I never could explain to my own satisfaction, why hernia did not as frequently take place into the sheath of the vein, as into the lymphatic sheath. As soon as I had traced the proper sheaths of these vessels, and examined their close connection with the edge of the crural arch, I at once perceived, that so long as these sheaths remain entire, no hernia can ever primarily pass into either, for the more the gut presses the peritoneum against the proper sheaths, so much the more firmly are the latter made to embrace the vessels. As the lymphatics have no proper sheath, there is less security against hernia passing into their portion of the common sheath, and accordingly, we seldom open the body of an aged female, without discovering a tendency to femoral hernia.

IN some rare cases, the proper sheath of the vein has been found wanting interior to Paupart's ligament, and in this case, hernia may as readily take place into the venous, as it usually does into the lymphatic sheath. When this happens, in a person in whom the obturator artery comes off by the short origin from the epigastric artery, the former vessel will to a certainty encircle the pubal side of the neck of the sac. If however, the obturator artery and the epigastric continue connected for a considerable distance from their origin, and if one herniary tumour pass into the sheath of the vein, and another escapes into the common sheath of the lymphatics, then both sacs may be traversed on their upper margins by the obturator artery, and the tumour in the lymphatic sheath, will likewise have the same vessel on its pubal side. I have never seen this variety in the course of the obturator artery, but I dissected the body of an aged woman last summer, in which I found one sac in the sheath of the lymphatics, and another in the sheath of the vein. In this subject, the obturator and epigastric arteries, came off by a short trunk from the external iliac, and the obturator in its way to the thyroid foramen, encircled the neck of the sac contained in the venous sheath. This new variety of arrangement of the obturator artery shews, that the general opinion respecting the safety of cutting toward the pubis, in those cases where the conjoined trunk of the epigastric and obturator is short, is not well founded. In this female we have seen, that although the common trunk of these vessels be very short, yet from the ilial tumour descending into the sheath of the vein, the neck of that sac is encircled by the obturator artery.

HAD strangulation taken place in this person in the pubal tumour, we might have operated with great ease and safety in Gimbernat's mode; had the ilial tumour however become incarcerated, and had we attempted in this case, to cut inward toward the pubis, we might without doubt, have divided the obturator artery. The peculiarity of the hernia in this woman is highly deserving of attention. Had a surgeon been called to see this person before death, he would have very readily discovered the pubal hernia; but from the locality and connection of the ilial tumour, it might very probably have eluded his notice. The sac was small, it could not have admitted more than the semi-diameter of the gut, and besides, it was deep seated; it was covered first by the integuments, over it was spread the loose glandular fascia, and the fascia lata, and between them there were lodged several conglobate glands, and below the deep fascia the sac was covered by the common and proper sheaths of the vein. From the number of coverings which the tumour had, and from its uncommon position and small size, it would on the living subject, have been extremely difficult to have discovered it.

To operate in such a case, without injuring the large obturator artery, would have been a matter of difficulty: The presence of this vessel would have been easily ascertained during the operation, for it was protruded so far, as to lie between the fascia lata, and the inverted, or sharp edge of Paupart's ligament, which in this female was peculiarly thick and strong, and exactly resembled what Mr. Hey describes as the femoral ligament. From this protrusion of the obturator artery, it might have been felt beating pretty low on the forepart of the sac, and with care it might have been so raised over a blunt hook, as to have allowed of the division of either Hey's ligament or the neck of the sac. As the operation is usually performed, the vessel would have suffered.

IN two subjects, I have found the obturator artery rising from the superficial femoral artery, at the distance of two inches below Paupart's ligament. In its course to the obturator foramen, it mounted along the pectineal aponeurosis, on the pubal side of the great vein, and entered the pelvis by the crural hole along with the lymphatics. As soon as it had entered the pelvis, it abruptly turned over the bone to the thyroid aperture. In this variety, the artery would have been placed on the posterior part of the sac in crural hernia.

THE epigastric artery is likewise unusual in its origin and course in some subjects, although it is on the whole, more rare to meet with a lusus of this vessel than of the obturator artery: and even when we do find such a lusus, it is less concerned in general in the performance of any surgical operation. The epigastric artery commonly rises from the external iliac, just where that vessel is about to pass beneath Paupart's ligament: sometimes however, it comes off much higher, and in a few rare instances, it has been found originating from the superficial femoral artery. That lusus in which the epigastric artery rises high on the external iliac vessel, is of no practical importance, but when the epigastric comes off from the superficial femoral artery, it may in its way back to the abdomen, be cut in performing the operation for crural hernia. I have met with one or two subjects, in which this vessel came off from the femoral artery, and made a sudden sweep backwards, ascending along the pubal side of the femoral vein, and entering the belly by the crural foramen. In its passage from the femoral artery to the crural hole, it lay in contact with the anterior face of the sheath of the lymphatics, therefore, had hernia protruded into this sheath, this vessel must have been placed on the forepart of the sac. From this situation of the artery, it would without care, be extremely liable to injury during the operation for hernia, but if cut in this place, we would easily have had it in our power to secure the artery by ligature.

THERE is another peculiarity sometimes met with in the course of the epigastric artery, even where its origin is natural; I allude to that variety in which the vessel is so long, that it forms a loop which passes down into the sheath of the lymphatics, and which may be compared to the prolapsus of the umbilical cord before the head of the fœtus during delivery. In this mode of

distribution of the artery, which is of rare occurrence, were crural hernia to take place in
the sheath of the lymphatics, the vessel would
be protruded on the forepart of the sac, and
might without caution be divided during the
operation, an accident more unpleasant to the
Surgeon than dangerous to the patient. The
very circumstance of the protrusion of the artery renders it easy to pass a thread round it.

THE arteria circumflexa ilii is a large vessel,
in general destined to wind round the crista ilii,
and to effect a junction with the arteria ilio-
lumbalis. It uniformly gives off a branch as it
passes by the anterior superior spine of the ilium,
which ascends in an oblique course, in the direction of a line drawn from the spine of the ilium
to the umbilicus. Sometimes this branch is
small, but at other times it is so large as almost
entirely to anihilate the branch of the vessel
which ought to follow the course of the crista
ilii. When this lusus is present, the large ascending branch of the circumflex artery may be
wounded in performing the operation of paracentesis of the abdomen. In one case, I saw
its accompanying vein opened by the trocar.
The patient, a young woman, had the operation
performed six times, and in all of them the perforation was made midway between the spine
of the ilium and the umbilicus. At each time,
the trocar was entered within the eighth part of
an inch of where it had formerly passed. In
the four first operations, the fluid was very

readily removed without the effusion of any blood, but in removing the water the fifth time, it was found tinged with blood, and when the canula was withdrawn, a stream of venous blood issued from the wound. The farther effusion of blood was prevented by regulated pressure by the eighteen tailed bandage.

On inspecting the body after death, it was found, that the stilet had punctured the ascending branch of the vena circumflexa ilii, which was preternaturally large. I mention this, for the purpose of observing, that many while undergoing the operation of paracentesis at this spot, have been troubled with an obstinate bleeding, which has uniformly been conjectured to arise from injury of the epigastric artery. If however this vessel has ever been injured while performing the operation at this place, it must have run in a very curious direction. It is more probable, that the preternaturally large ascending branch of the circumflex artery had been the one hurt. It is sometimes as large as the epigastric artery, and it always lies in the direct line of operation. The usual place therefore where the trocar is entered in this country, is among the very worst which could have been selected; the operation may, as in the London hospitals, be much more safely performed in the space between the pubis and the umbilicus.

In the arm, the humeral artery very often divides into the radial and ulnar branches, even near to the axilla. In the iliac artery we seldom see an analogous lusus to this. In three bodies which I have lately dissected, and in one which I dissected formerly, the iliac artery divided into the femoral and profunda vessels, before it escaped from the pelvis. This is however by no means of frequent occurrence, nor is it a lusus of much practical importance.

THE arteria circumflexa interna, in a young subject which I examined about five months ago, originated from the external iliac artery above Paupart's ligament, and passed through the crural foramen in its way to the muscles about the top of the thigh. It ran along the front of of the lymphatic sheath, so that had crural hernia taken place in this person, and had an operation been required, this artery would most probably have been divided, but like the epigastric when it rises from the femoral artery, it would have been easily secured. When the internal circumflex artery originates from the external iliac, it is only in danger of injury when the gut protrudes into the sheath of the lymphatics. I have seen one instance in which the circumflex artery rose from the femoral artery, a little below the crural arch, and in this instance, it traversed the front of the common sheath of the great vein, and also of the lymphatics. Had hernia therefore taken place either into the lymphatic or venous sheaths, the forepart of the sac must have been crossed by this artery, which during the performance of the operation would have been exposed to danger.

THE superficial femoral artery, in general separates from the profunda at the distance of from one to two inches below Paupart's ligament, it is seldom so low as four inches, though Mr. Bell states this as the medium point. From this assertion, I infer that Mr. Bell has described this artery from dried preparations, in which, from the retraction of Paupart's ligament, the origin of the profunda seems to take place lower than on the recent subject. In a well formed person, the superficial femoral artery is not overlapped by the pubal margin of the sartorius muscle, till it has got to the distance of four inches below the crural arch. Below this, both the superficial femoral, and the profunda arteries are covered by this muscle. If therefore, we admit Mr. Bell's statement of the arteria profunda not arising till four inches below Paupart's ligament, we must of necessity, in the operation for popliteal aneurism, take up the superficial femoral artery in the second, instead of the lower part of the first, or upper third division of the thigh, and in doing this, before we could reach the artery, we must either tediously dissect back, or cut through the sartorius muscle. Some late writers on anatomy, recommend that the inner or pubal edge of this muscle, should be taken as our guide in the performance of the operation for popliteal aneurism. This may be perfectly correct, provided the pelvis be well formed, and we make the cision in the upper third of the thigh; if however, the cut be made lower, or if the anterior superior spine be carried toward the pubis, the sartorius, instead of directing us to the vessel, will lead us astray. In the second third of the thigh, the femoral artery is naturally covered by the sartorius, and when the spine of the ilium is much curved forward, the muscle prematurely overlaps it. Where the person was otherwise well formed, I have seen the spine of the ilium so much turned toward the pubis, that the sartorius covered the femoral artery, before it had reached two inches below Paupart's ligament. In taking up the femoral artery, whoever trusts to the direction of the sartorius muscle, will in some cases be embarrassed; for where the muscle is nearer the pubis than it ought to be, he will find it very difficult to determine during the operation, the precise spot where he has hit the muscle, or to resolve whether to dissect on the ilial or pubal side of the sartorius. If the incision be in any case made a little to the ilial margin of the triceps longus, the artery even although covered by the sartorius, is easily got at; we only require to follow the slope of the adductor muscles as we penetrate deeper; if we do this, we cannot miss the artery. If any guide be necessary, the triceps longus is more certain than the sartorius, which varies in its relation to the artery, according to the greater or less curvature of the spine of the ilium.

THE tibial and peroneal arteries are subject to variations in their origin and course, and in some subjects, we even find one or other of these vessels altogether wanting. The deviations however, met with in the vascular system of the leg and foot, are more matter of curiosity, than of practical importance, and do not therefore require to be particularized.

IN the preceding Observations on the unusual origin and course of the large arteries, I have chiefly confined my attention to the history of such deviations, as have a tendency to illustrate some point in pathology, or which are proper to be known before operating on the living body. I have now only to add, that all the descriptions, with the exception of a single one on the authority of my friend Dr. Barclay, are taken from dissections made by myself, or from preparations in my possession.

THE END.

JAMES MUIRHEAD, *Printer.*